Example MATHEMATICS FOR GCSE

FOR GCSE

Foundation Level

Ewart Smith MSc

Head of Mathematics Department
Tredegar Comprehensive School

Stanley Thornes (Publishers) Ltd

First published in 1988 by:
Stanley Thornes (Publishers) Ltd
Old Station Drive
Leckhampton
CHELTENHAM GL53 0DN
England

Reprinted 1989
Reprinted 1990
Reprinted 1991
Reprinted 1992

British Library Cataloguing in Publication Data

Smith, Ewart
    Examples in mathematics for GCSE foundation level.
    1. Mathematics — For schools
    I. Title
    510

    ISBN 0-85950-706-8

Typeset in 12pt Aldine by Tech-Set, Gateshead, Tyne & Wear.
Printed and bound in Great Britain at The Bath Press, Avon.

Contents

Preface

The aim of this book is to provide a reservoir of examples for fourth-year and fifth-year students studying for the foundation level of the GCSE examinations.

The book is divided into four parts:

PART 1 provides exercises on individual topics and forms the basis of a fourth-year course.

PART 2 consists of 20 revision papers which, together with specimen papers and past papers, will be sufficient for the fifth year.

PART 3 contains 8 exercises of multiple choice questions. This type of question is extremely useful as a teaching aid, and is included in the examination arrangements of some of the examining boards.

PART 4 gives 10 aural tests. It is not intended that the pupils work these out independently. The teacher, or some other person, should read the questions to the pupils. No more than about 20 seconds should be spent on each question. A calculator should not be used for this work.

The answers are available as a separately published booklet.

My thanks are due to my colleague Allan Snelgrove BSc for checking the answers and making several useful suggestions, and British Telecommunications for the sample bill on page 64. Finally, I would like to thank the staff of Stanley Thornes (Publishers) Ltd for their kind help and enthusiasm during the production of this book.

Ewart Smith
1988

Part 1: Exercises

Whole Number Arithmetic **1**

Write in figures the numbers

1 forty-two

2 one hundred and seventy

3 three hundred and thirty-seven

4 five hundred and nine

5 seven hundred and eleven

6 six thousand eight hundred and seventeen

7 two thousand three hundred

8 eight thousand and fifty seven

9 two million

10 eight hundred thousand

Write in words the numbers

11	66	12	72	13	239	14	583
15	126	16	416	17	2934	18	7165
19	37 000	20	150 000				

What is the remainder when

21 24 is divided by 7, 22 36 is divided by 8,

23 50 is divided by 10, 24 29 is divided by 9,

25 100 is divided by 8?

What must be added to

26 5×9 to make 50, 27 7×4 to make 30,

28 9×8 to make 75, 29 60 to make 8×8,

30 35 to make 7×7?

Find the value of

31 $(5 \times 3) + (4 \times 6)$ 32 $(7 \times 5) - (2 \times 9)$

33 $5^2 + 9^2$ 34 $8^2 - 4^2$

35 $8 \times 7 + 3$ 36 $6 \times 8 - 4$

37 Write the prime numbers between 20 and 40.

38 Write the whole numbers between 20 and 40 that are exactly divisible by 6.

39 Write the whole numbers between 30 and 60 that are exactly divisible by 7.

40 Find two numbers whose sum is 13 that, when multiplied together, give 42.

41 Find two numbers whose sum is 15 that, when multiplied together, give 56.

42 Find two numbers whose difference is 1 that, when multiplied together, give 30.

43 Find two numbers whose difference is 4 that, when multiplied together, give 21.

44 Which is the larger, 13×7 or 8×12?

45 Which is the smaller, 21×18 or 19×20?

46 What is the value of the 3 in the number 5307?

47 What is the value of the 5 in the number 45 274?

48 Write the number 48 738 correct to
(a) the nearest 100,   (b) the nearest 1000.

49 Round off the following numbers correct to the nearest 1000.
(a) 25 345   (b) 86 952   (c) 147 392

50 The report on a football match said that 63 000 people had attended, correct to the nearest thousand.
(a) What is the largest number that could have been present?
(b) What is the smallest number that could have been present?

51 In a knock-out competition there are 16 teams.
(a) How many matches must be played in the first round?
(b) How many matches must be played in the second round?
(c) How many matches must be played to find the winner of the competition?
(d) How many rounds are required to reach the semi-finals?
(e) The following year an extra team joins the competition. How can they solve the problem of having 17 teams in the first round?

(In this question assume that no match is drawn.)

Patterns

Write the next two numbers in each of the following patterns.

1	6, 10, 14, 18	2	6, 11, 16, 21
3	1, 3, 6, 10	4	1, 4, 9, 16
5	1, 5, 25, 125	6	3, 12, 48, 192
7	40, 34, 28, 22	8	2, 5, 10, 17
9	256, 128, 64, 32	10	6, 9, 14, 21

Give the next two arrangements in each of the following patterns.

11

 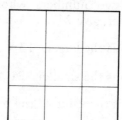

12

  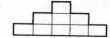

13

 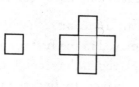 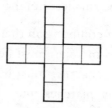

14

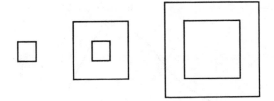

Negative Numbers 3

In questions 1 to 8 place the correct symbol, > or <, between the given pairs of numbers.

1	5	−7	**2**	−3	4	**3**	−5	8
4	9	−3	**5**	7	−10	**6**	−4	−3
7	−5	−2	**8**	−7	−10			

9 Rearrange the numbers −5, 4, 8, −9 in order of size, smallest first.

10 Rearrange the numbers −7, −10, −4, 2 in order of size, largest first.

11 Rearrange the numbers 4, −6, −7, −3 in order of size, smallest first.

12 Rearrange the numbers 12, −13, 11, −10 in order of size, largest first.

13 At 3 p.m. the temperature was 4°C. By midnight it had fallen to −3°C. How much did it fall?

14 The reading on a thermometer is −4°C. If the temperature falls by 4°C, what is the new temperature?

15 Copy and complete the table which shows the temperature, at two-hourly intervals, in Filsham one day last winter.

Time	6 a.m.	8 a.m.	10 a.m.	12 noon	2 p.m.	4 p.m.	6 p.m.
Temperature (in °C)	−7	−4	2	4	7	0	−3
Change since previous reading	−	+3	+6				

(a) What was the greatest rise between two readings next to each other?

(b) What was the difference between the highest and lowest temperatures recorded?

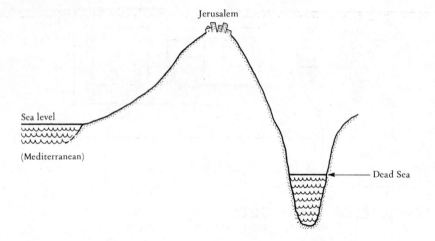

The diagram shows the positions of Jerusalem, the Dead Sea and the Mediterranean Sea. Jerusalem is 820 m above sea level. The Dead Sea is 430 m below sea level and is 430 m deep.

(a) How high is Jerusalem above the level of the Dead Sea?

(b) How much is the level of the Mediterranean Sea above the bottom of the Dead Sea?

(c) Which is the larger rise vertically, from the bottom of the Dead Sea to sea level or from sea level to Jerusalem?

(d) An aeroplane flies at 200 m above the Dead Sea. How much is this below sea level?

Fractions   4

In questions 1 to 9, what fraction of each shape is shaded?

1

2
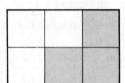

3

4
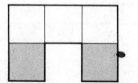

5

6
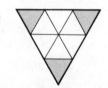

7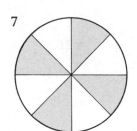

8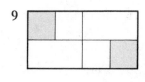

9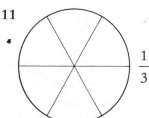

In questions 10 to 13, copy each figure and shade the given fraction.

10 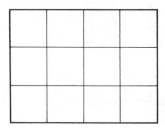 $\dfrac{5}{6}$

11 $\dfrac{1}{3}$

12 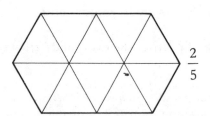 $\dfrac{2}{5}$

13 $\dfrac{3}{8}$

14 Fill in the missing numbers.

   (a) $\dfrac{3}{4} = \dfrac{}{12}$ (b) $\dfrac{2}{5} = \dfrac{}{20}$ (c) $\dfrac{8}{10} = \dfrac{}{5}$

   (d) $\dfrac{5}{6} = \dfrac{15}{}$ (e) $\dfrac{}{5} = \dfrac{24}{30}$ (f) $\dfrac{3}{8} = \dfrac{15}{}$

15 Change these top-heavy fractions into mixed numbers.

   (a) $\dfrac{3}{2}$ (b) $\dfrac{9}{4}$ (c) $\dfrac{11}{3}$ (d) $\dfrac{21}{5}$ (e) $\dfrac{15}{9}$

16 Change these mixed numbers into top-heavy fractions.

   (a) $2\frac{1}{5}$ (b) $1\frac{4}{5}$ (c) $3\frac{1}{3}$ (d) $4\frac{5}{6}$ (e) $1\frac{3}{4}$

17 Find

   (a) $\frac{1}{2} + \frac{1}{3}$ (b) $\frac{1}{3} + \frac{1}{4}$ (c) $\frac{2}{3} + \frac{1}{4}$ (d) $\frac{3}{4} + \frac{2}{5}$

18 Find

   (a) $\frac{1}{2} - \frac{1}{3}$ (b) $\frac{1}{3} - \frac{1}{4}$ (c) $\frac{3}{4} - \frac{2}{3}$ (d) $\frac{2}{5} - \frac{3}{10}$

19 Find

    (a) $2 \times \frac{3}{4}$ (b) $3 \times \frac{5}{9}$ (c) $\frac{7}{12} \times 4$ (d) $\frac{3}{5} \times 10$

20 Find

    (a) $\frac{1}{2} \times \frac{2}{3}$ (b) $\frac{3}{4} \times \frac{2}{5}$ (c) $2\frac{2}{5} \times \frac{3}{4}$ (d) $1\frac{2}{5} \times 2\frac{1}{2}$

21 Find

    (a) $2 \div \frac{1}{2}$ (b) $3 \div \frac{3}{5}$ (c) $\frac{4}{5} \div \frac{3}{10}$ (d) $1\frac{1}{3} \div \frac{4}{5}$

22 Find

    (a) 75p as a fraction of £1,

    (b) 64 cm as a fraction of 1 m,

    (c) 15 minutes as a fraction of 1 hour,

    (d) 6 hours as a fraction of 1 day,

    (e) 2 right angles as a fraction of a complete turn,

    (f) 2 ft as a fraction of 1 yd.

23 In a class of 25 pupils, $\frac{3}{5}$ are girls. How many boys are there?

24 Peter eats $\frac{1}{3}$ of his sweets and has 12 left. How many did he have to start with?

25 Neil spends $\frac{1}{2}$ of his money on food and $\frac{1}{3}$ on a record. What fraction does he have left? If this fraction amounts to £2, how much money did he have to start with?

26 Shavi poured $\frac{3}{?}$ of a can of oil into the engine of his car. He had 5 litres left over. How much did he use?

27 How many jars each of which holds $\frac{1}{2}$ kg, can be filled from a tin of jam holding 21 kg?

28 The area of a blackboard is $7\frac{1}{2}$ m². It is $1\frac{1}{2}$ m wide. How long is it?

29 Rachel saves £3.50 a week to buy a radio costing £42. What fraction has she saved after 8 weeks?

30 In a school election there were two candidates. Allan got $\frac{5}{12}$ of the votes and Beryl got $\frac{1}{3}$. A total of 300 pupils did not vote.

    (a) What fraction of the pupils   (i) voted,   (ii) did not vote?

    (b) How many pupils are there in the school?

    (c) How many votes did Beryl get?

Decimals

1. Write these fractions as decimals.
   (a) $\frac{4}{10}$ (b) $\frac{23}{100}$ (c) $\frac{3}{5}$ (d) $\frac{7}{25}$ (e) $\frac{12}{10}$

2. Write the place value of the 5 in
   (a) 53.1 (b) 147.5 (c) 12.05 (d) 507.6

3. Write the place value of the 8 in
   (a) 0.428 (b) 181.4 (c) 15.82 (d) 1800

4. Find
   (a) 53.6×10 (b) 0.4×100 (c) 1.04×1000
   (d) $79.2 \div 10$ (e) $46.3 \div 100$ (f) $4.9 \div 1000$

5. Find
   (a) $5.26 + 7.93$ (b) $16.42 + 1.97$ (c) $9.37 + 24.4$
   (d) $16.4 + 9.43 + 2.09$

6. Find
   (a) $26.4 - 9.7$ (b) $137.2 - 63.42$ (c) $9 - 0.47$

7. Find
   (a) 4.23×5 (b) 0.73×30 (c) 8.43×70
   (d) 7.6×3.9 (e) 26.2×5.4 (f) 36.3×14.9

8. Find
   (a) $23.79 \div 3$ (b) $31.4 \div 5$ (c) $31.05 \div 6.9$
   (d) $67.24 \div 8.2$ (e) $14.98 \div 0.7$ (f) $4.29 \div 0.066$

9. From a plank of wood 5 m long, Harry cuts one piece 1.7 m long and another piece 2.54 m long. What length remains?

10. Karen's car travels 94.5 km on 7.5 litres of petrol. How many kilometres per litre is this?

11. A sheet of paper is 29.4 cm long and 21.7 cm wide. What is
    (a) its perimeter, (b) its area?

12. A lorry weighs 2.54 t. It is loaded with 30 boxes each weighing 0.046 t. Find
    (a) the total weight of the boxes,
    (b) the total weight of the loaded lorry.

13. From a 500 cm length of tape, Sally cuts pieces 31.25 cm long. How many complete pieces will she obtain?

14   The instructions on a bag of fertiliser state that it should be used at the rate of 0.04 kg to the square metre. What area will a 2 kg bag of fertiliser cover?

15   A wine bottle holds 0.7 litres of wine. How many glasses can be filled from this bottle, if each glass holds 0.0875 litres?

Percentages   6

1   Express each percentage as a decimal.
    (a) 50%   (b) 75%   (c) 60%   (d) 34%

2   Express each percentage as a fraction in its lowest terms.
    (a) 25%   (b) 80%   (c) 45%   (d) 12%

3   Convert each fraction into (i) a percentage, (ii) a decimal.
    (a) $\frac{1}{2}$ (b) $\frac{3}{4}$ (c) $\frac{4}{5}$ (d) $\frac{7}{10}$

4   Convert each decimal into (i) a percentage, (ii) a fraction in its lowest terms.
    (a) 0.2   (b) 0.25   (c) 0.85   (d) 0.44

5   In an English test, Sian scores 12 out of 20. What percentage is this?

6   Eighty per cent of the families in a street take morning papers. What fraction is this?

7   Ninety-six of the 120 houses in a street have telephones. What percentage is this?

8   In a school, 11 out of every 20 pupils are boys. What percentage of the pupils are
    (a) boys,   (b) girls?

9   Express the first quantity as a percentage of the second.
    (a) 60p, 120p   (b) 24 cm, 50 cm
    (c) 35p, £1.75   (d) 80 cm, 2 m

10 Ruslan paid £11 deposit on a record player. The cash price of the record player was £55. What percentage of the cash price was needed as a deposit?

11

(a) The marked price of a jumper is £24. What is the sale price?
(b) The marked price of a coat is £64. What is the sale price?
(c) The marked price of a computer is £252. What is the sale price?

12 Alf bought two video recorders for £400 each.
(a) He sold one to Ben at a profit of 20%. What did Ben pay for it?
(b) He sold the other to Claire at a loss of 10%. What did Claire pay for it?

13 Laura earns £120 per week. She is promised a rise of 10%. What will her new weekly wage be?

14 My telephone bill is £68 plus value added tax (VAT) at 15%. How much must I pay British Telecom?

15

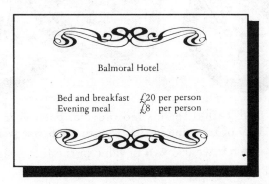

Two people stay at this hotel for one night. VAT is added to the bill at 15%. How much is the total cost, if they also take the evening meal?

16

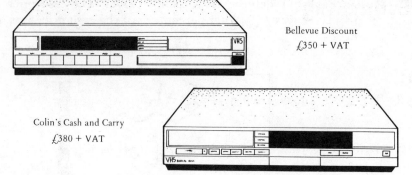

Bellevue Discount
£350 + VAT

Colin's Cash and Carry
£380 + VAT

(a) Paul buys a video at Bellevue Discount. If VAT is 15%, how much does he pay for it?

(b) Lorna buys her video at Colin's Cash and Carry. How much does she pay for it?

(c) Donna buys her video at Bellevue Discount but, because she pays cash, is given a discount of 5%. How much does she pay for her video? (Don't forget to include the VAT.)

17 Phyllis earns an annual wage of £11 500. Her total tax allowances are £3400. Find

(a) her taxable income,

(b) the amount of tax due when the rate of tax is
(i) 25%,   (ii) 40%.

18

Andrew paid £4000 for his motorcycle. Each year it went down in value by 10% of its value at the beginning of that year. Find

(a) how much it went down in value in the first year,

(b) what it was worth when it was one year old,

(c) how much it went down in value in the second year,

(d) what it was worth when it was two years old.

Estimating

1   Write each of the given numbers correct to the nearest 10.
   (a) 57.2   (b) 546   (c) 2378   (d) 89.7

2   Write each of the given numbers correct to the nearest 100.
   (a) 213   (b) 758   (c) 3492   (d) 17 673

3   Write each of the given numbers correct to the nearest 1000.
   (a) 37 423   (b) 54 612   (c) 9399   (d) 19 902

4   Write each of the given decimals correct to one decimal place.
   (a) 3.724   (b) 15.394   (c) 27.526   (d) 1.7782

5   Find a rough estimate for
   (a) $48.2 \div 15.9$ (b) 8.73×21.7 (c) 4.97^2
   (d) $\dfrac{27.4 \times 1.92}{14.73}$ (e) $\dfrac{8.07 \times 1.82}{12.13}$ (f) $\dfrac{10.03}{4.97 \times 2.1}$

6   A therm of gas costs 38.4 p. Estimate the cost of 523 therms.

7   The crowd at a match was 78 512. Give the attendance correct to
   (a) the nearest 1000,   (b) the nearest 100.

8   The attendance at a cricket match was 15 600, correct to the nearest
   hundred. What was
   (a) the largest number of people that could have been present,
   (b) the smallest number that could have been present?

9
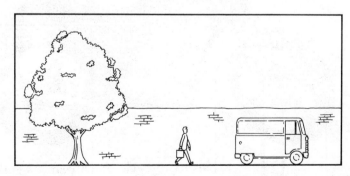

Study the diagram.

Assuming that the man is 1.8 m tall, estimate
   (a) the height of the tree,
   (b) the length of the van,
   (c) the height of the wall,
   (d) the length of the wall shown.

10

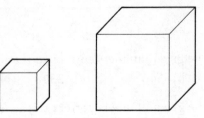

Estimate the number of small cubes required to fill completely the space within the large cube.

11 Tommy Wright requires

>49 m of timber at 52p per metre
>81 tiles at 38p each
>3 bags of cement at £4.15 per bag
>15 cwt of sand at £1.10 per hundredweight

Tommy has £100 to spend. Estimate whether or not Tommy has enough money.

12 Estimate the size of each of the following angles.

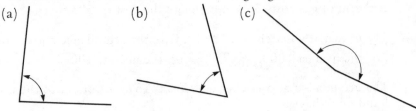

13 Draw a line that you think is about 5 cm long. Measure it to see how good your estimate is.

14

The milk bottle is 18 cm high. Estimate
(a) the height of the wine bottle,
(b) the height of the cup,
(c) the diameter of the saucer,
(d) the height of the packet of cornflakes.

15

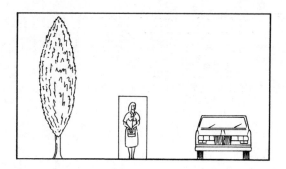

The woman in the picture is about 1.6 m tall. Estimate
(a) the height of the tree,
(b) the width of the doorway,
(c) the width of the car.

Geometry 8

1 Say whether each of the given angles is acute, obtuse or reflex.
(a)

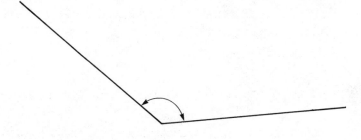

(b)

(c)

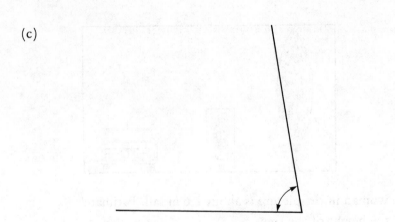

(d)

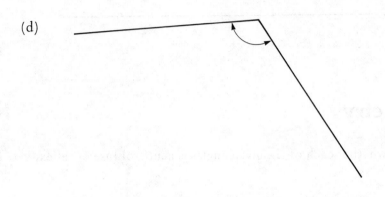

(e)

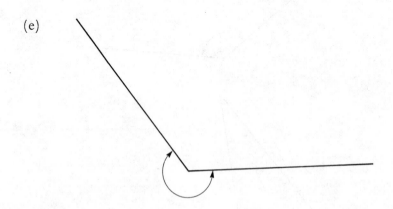

2   Use your protractor to measure each of the angles given in question 1.

16

In questions 3 to 20, find the angles marked with letters.

3

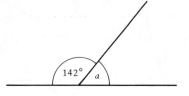

142° a

4

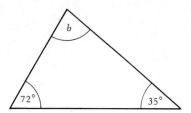

b

72°   35°

5

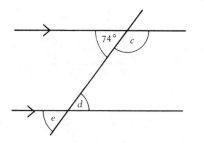

74° c

d

e

6

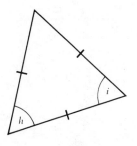

g

68°   f

7

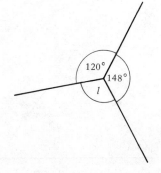

i

h

8

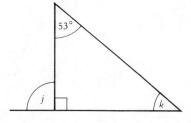

53°

j   k

9

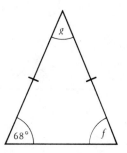

120°
148°

l

10

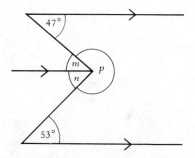

47°

m
p
n

53°

11

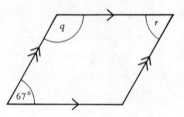

12

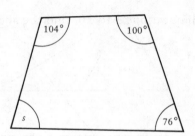

13

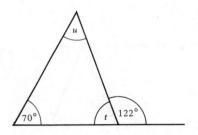

14

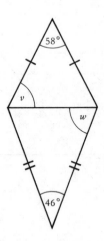

15

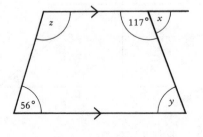

16

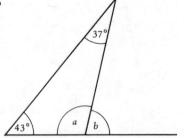

17

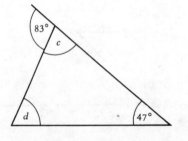

18

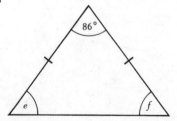

18

19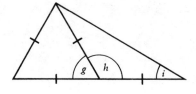

20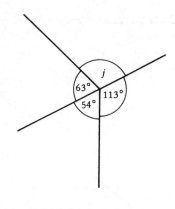

Measurement and Units   9

1   Measure each of the following lines to the nearest centimetre (cm).
   (a) ————————————

   (b) ——————————————————————

   (c) ————————————————

   (d) ——————

2   Measure each of the following lines to the nearest millimetre (mm).
   (a) ——————————————

   (b) ————————————————————

   (c) ——————————————————————

   (d) ——————————

3   Use a straight edge without a scale to draw a line approximately
   (a) 5 cm long,   (b) 10 cm long,
   (c) 7 cm long,   (d) 40 mm long.

4

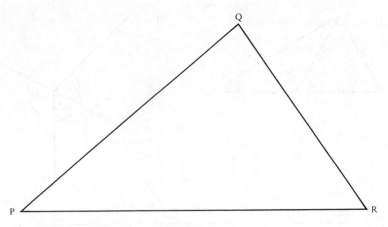

(a) Measure the sides of this triangle.
(b) What is the perimeter of this triangle?
(c) Measure the angles in this triangle.
(d) What is the sum of these angles?

5 (a) Measure the sides of this triangle.
  (b) Find the perimeter of this triangle.
  (c) Measure the angles of this triangle.
  (d) What is the sum of these three angles?

6 (a) Measure, in millimetres, the diameter of this circle.
  (b) The circumference of this circle is found by multiplying the diameter by 3.14. What is the circumference of this circle?

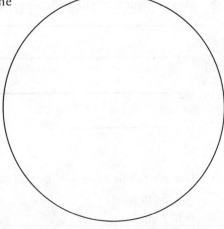

7 ABC is an isosceles triangle.
   (a) Measure the length of (i) AB, (ii) AC, (iii) BC.
   (b) Find the perimeter of this triangle.
   (c) Find the size of the angle marked x.

8 The diagram shows an arrowhead.
   Use your protractor to measure
   (a) x   (b) y   (c) z

9

   (a) Measure, in millimetres,
        the lengths of AB, AC and BC.
   (b) Find the perimeter of this
        triangle.
   (c) Use your protractor to measure the size of each of the angles.
   (d) What is the sum of the three angles in this triangle?

10
        Use your protractor to find the size of the
        angles marked x, y and z.

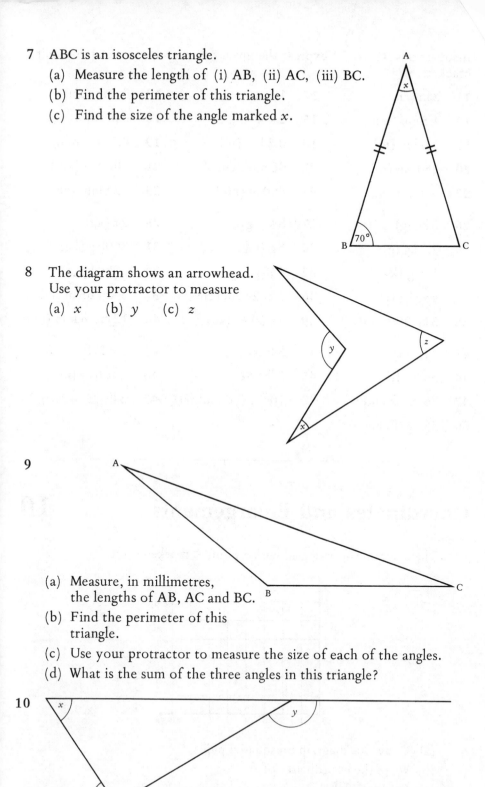

21

In questions 11 to 50 express the given quantity in terms of the unit in brackets.

11	3 m (cm)	12	18 cm (mm)	13	5.1 m (cm)
14	4.5 cm (mm)	15	2 km (m)	16	6 m (mm)
17	1.6 km (m)	18	0.3 km (m)	19	0.7 cm (mm)
20	250 cm (m)	21	60 mm (cm)	22	7000 m (km)
23	430 cm (m)	24	850 m (km)	25	123 mm (cm)
26	3 kg (g)	27	8 kg (g)	28	2 t (kg)
29	4.5 kg (g)	30	5 g (mg)	31	3000 g (kg)
32	500 g (kg)	33	750 g (kg)	34	5000 kg (t)
35	450 kg (t)	36	1 m 24 cm (cm)	37	3 km 65 m (m)
38	5 kg 200 g (g)	39	2 t 50 kg (kg)	40	12 cm 8 mm (mm)
41	3 ft (in)	42	5 ft (in)	43	2 yd (ft)
44	36 in (ft)	45	5 lb (oz)	46	2 ft 6 in (in)
47	76 in (ft and in)	48	100 ft (yd and ft)	49	3 lb 12 oz (oz)
50	36 oz (lb and oz)				

Coordinates and Enlargements   10

1   The diagram shows a grid with a point A marked on it.

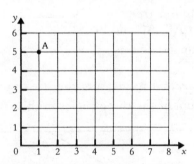

(a) Copy this diagram on squared paper.
(b) Write the coordinates of A.
(c) Mark and label the points B(3, 1) and C(7, 3).
(d) Join the points with straight lines to give triangle ABC.
(e) Write the coordinates of the midpoint of AC.

2 (a) Copy this diagram on squared paper.

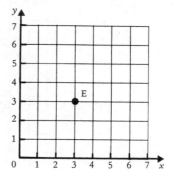

   (b) Plot the points A(2, 0), B(6, 2), C(4, 6) and D(0, 4). Join these points to give a quadrilateral ABCD.

   (c) What name do we give to this quadrilateral?

   (d) Measure the length of AB and hence write down the area of this quadrilateral.

   (e) What special point is E?

3

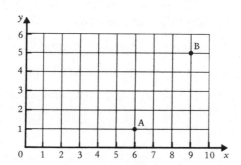

(a) Copy this diagram on squared paper.

(b) Write the coordinates of the points A and B.

(c) Plot the points C(4, 5) and D(1, 1).

(d) Join the points with straight lines to give a quadrilateral ABCD.

(e) Measure each of the sides of this quadrilateral. What special name do we give to it?

(f) How many lines of symmetry does this quadrilateral have?

(g) Does the quadrilateral have rotational symmetry? If so, state the order.

(h) Find the area of the quadrilateral.

4 (a) Copy the diagram. Write the coordinates of the points A, B and C.

   (b) Mark and label the point D(−2, 3). Join AD and DC. What kind of quadrilateral is ABCD?

   (c) How many axes of symmetry does this quadrilateral have?

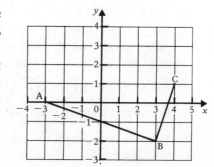

23

5

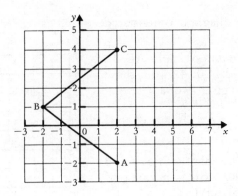

(a) Copy the diagram. Write the coordinates of A, B and C.

(b) Mark and label the point D so that all the sides of the quad-rilateral, ABCD, are the same length.

(c) What name do we give to this quadrilateral?

(d) How many axes of symmetry does ABCD have?

(e) Write down the area of triangle ABC and hence find the area of the quadrilateral.

6

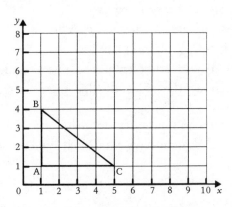

(a) Copy the diagram. Write the coordinates of A, B and C.

(b) Extend the line AB to a point D such that AB = BD, and produce AC to E such that AC = CE. Write the coordinates of D and E. Draw the triangle ADE.

(c) Find the area of triangle ABC.

(d) Find the area of triangle ADE.

(e) What is the ratio of the area of triangle ABC to the area of triangle ADE?

7 (a) Copy the diagram. Write the coordinates of the points A, B, C and D.

   (b) Extend AB to E so that AE = 3AB.

   (c) Extend AD to G so that AG = 3AD.

   (d) Write the coordinates of E and G.

   (e) Mark and label F so that AEFG is a rectangle.

   (f) What is the area of (i) ABCD, (ii) AEFG?

   (g) Express $\dfrac{\text{area ABCD}}{\text{area AEFG}}$ as a fraction in its lowest terms.

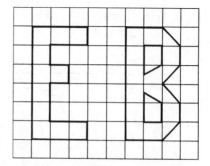

8 (a) Copy these letters on a sheet of 0.5 cm squared paper. (Note that more squares are needed than shown here.)

   (b) On the same grid, draw these letters so that they are twice this size.

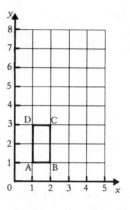

9

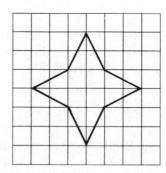

   (a) Copy this four-pointed star on a sheet of 1 cm squared paper.

   (b) By counting, or otherwise, find the area of the star.

   (c) Draw another star which is an enlargement of the first using a scale factor of 2.

   (d) Find the area of this larger star.

   (e) What is the ratio of the areas of the two stars?

25

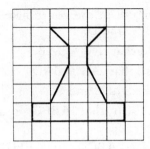

(a) Copy this shape on squared paper.

(b) By counting squares, find its area in square units.

(c) Draw an enlargement of this shape using a scale factor of 3.

(d) By counting squares, find the area of the enlargement in square units.

(e) What is the ratio of the area of the small shape to the area of the enlargement?

Earning Money 11

1   Peter is paid £2.30 an hour for his work on Saturdays in a local supermarket. He works from 8.00 in the morning until 5.30 in the afternoon. He has an hour off for lunch.

(a) How many hours does he work?

(b) How much does he earn?

2   Rose is paid £3 an hour. Each weekday, from Monday to Friday, she works from 8.30 a.m. to 5.30 p.m. She has an hour for lunch.

(a) How many hours does she work (i) in a day, (ii) each week?

(b) How much does she earn in a week?

3   Tina earns £87.50 in a week. She works 7 hours each weekday. She does not work on Saturday.

(a) How much is she paid for one day's work?

(b) How much an hour does she earn?

4   Tim is paid £3 per hour for the first 35 hours he works. Overtime is paid at 'time and a half'.
    (a) How much does Tim earn for a 35-hour week?
    (b) How much is he paid for each hour of overtime?
    (c) One week he worked 42 hours. How much pay did he get?
    (d) Another week he earned £114. How many hours overtime did Tim work?

5   Leslie works a basic week of 37 hours, for which he is paid £3.48 per hour.
    (a) Find his basic weekly wage.
    (b) He is paid 'double time' for overtime. How much will he earn for 3 hours overtime?

6   Here are three jobs from a local newspaper.

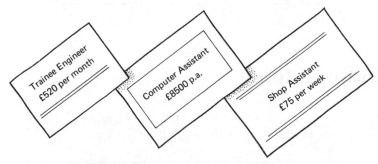

Trainee Engineer
£520 per month

Computer Assistant
£8500 p.a.

Shop Assistant
£75 per week

    (a) How much will the trainee engineer earn in a year?
    (b) How much will the shop assistant earn in a year of 52 weeks?
    (c) Which of the three jobs is the best paid?

7   For the first 35 hours Olive works in a week, she is paid at a basic rate of £5 per hour. For any hours more than 35 hours, she is paid at 'time and a half'. The table given below shows the number of hours Olive worked each day during a particular week.

Day	Mon.	Tue.	Wed.	Thur.	Fri.
Number of hours worked	7	8	8	10	7

    (a) How much does Olive earn for working 1 hour of overtime?
    (b) How many hours did she work during the week?
    (c) How many of these would she be paid at the overtime rate?
    (d) Find her basic weekly wage for working 35 hours.
    (e) Find the amount she earned as overtime.
    (f) Find her total earnings for the week.
    (g) If her deductions for the week came to £63.50, find her 'take-home' pay.

8   Mr Snook earns £12 400 in a year. His total tax allowances come to £4500.

   (a) Find his taxable income.

   (b) How much income tax does he pay when the rate of tax on his taxable income is 25%?

9   Jill Price earns £250 a week. She pays £12 in National Insurance contributions and is allowed an additional £50 per week free of income tax. Find

   (a) the total amount she does not pay tax on,

   (b) the amount on which tax is due – her taxable income,

   (c) the amount of income tax she pays if her taxable income is taxed at the rate of 27 p in the pound.

Spending Money   12

1   Peter buys four records at £1.10 each. How much does he have to pay? How much change will he get if he pays with a £5 note?

2

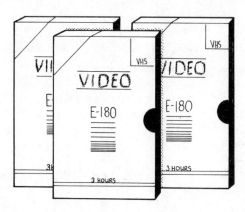

   Anne hires three videos at £1.20 each. How much will this cost her? How much change will she get from a £10 note?

3   Sarah buys a set of stamps for her collection. Their values are 18 p, 26 p, 31 p and 34 p. She pays with a £5 note. How much change will she get?

4   Bill buys eight 18 p stamps and seven 13 p stamps. How much will they cost? He pays with three £1 coins. How much change will he get?

| £1.24 | £2.40 | £3.48 |

5   Fiona wants 480 tea-bags.
   (a) How many boxes of 80 bags would she need?
   (b) Which is the cheapest way of buying 480 tea-bags?

6   Fresh Gate Dairies sell milk at 28p per pint, while Peacock Dairies charge 47p per litre.
   (a) If 1 litre = 1.75 pints, find the cost of 1 litre of milk from Fresh Gate Dairies.
   (b) Which dairy sells the more expensive milk?

7   A greengrocer buys a 50 kg bag of potatoes for £3.50, and sells them at 10p per kilogram. How much profit does she make?

8   Find the total cost of

   12 rolls of wallpaper at £7.20 per roll
   4 litres of paint at £2.20 per litre
   3 brushes at 95p each
   2 packets of paste at £1.20 each

9   During a certain four-week period, Len had £5 per week pocket money, earned £4.20, £4.80, £4.26 and £5.58 from his newspaper round and received a total of £6.16 for odd jobs.
   (a) Find his total income for the four weeks.
   (b) What was his average income per week?

10 The price of admission to an exhibition is £4.50 for adults and half-price for children.
   (a) What is the price of admission for a child?
   (b) How much will it cost for a father, mother and three children to go into the exhibition?
   (c) Mother pays with a £20 note. How much change will she get?

11 Lisa buys a tumble dryer on hire-purchase (HP). A deposit of £56 is required, together with 24 monthly payments of £10.30.
   (a) Find the total HP price.
   (b) If the cash price is £260, how much is saved by paying cash?

12 A householder decides to buy a 22 in colour TV set that is marked '£232 cash or £58 deposit + 24 monthly payments of £9.88'. He decides to use the second method. Find

(a) the total value of the 24 monthly payments,

(b) the total price of the TV set using the second method,

(c) the amount saved by paying cash.

13 Some silk is sold at £18.30 per metre. From a roll of the silk 50 m long, 12 pieces each 4.1 m long are cut off.

(a) What length of silk is left on the roll?

(b) What is the value of this piece?

14 The tables show the approximate cost, in pounds per square foot of ground area, for rebuilding semi-detached houses. The country is divided into four regions. The cost of rebuilding varies with the size and age of the house.

		Pre-1920		
		Large	Medium	Small
Typical area (in ft²)		2300	1650	1200
Cost (in £ per ft²)	Region 1	49.50	50.50	50.50
	Region 2	43.50	44.50	44.00
	Region 3	41.50	42.00	42.00
	Region 4	39.00	40.00	40.00

		1920–45		
		Large	Medium	Small
Typical area (in ft²)		1350	1150	900
Cost (in £ per ft²)	Region 1	52.50	50.50	50.50
	Region 2	46.00	44.50	44.50
	Region 3	43.50	42.00	42.00
	Region 4	41.50	40.00	40.00

		1946–present		
		Large	Medium	Small
Typical area (in ft²)		1650	1350	1050
Cost (in £ per ft²)	Region 1	37.50	40.00	42.50
	Region 2	33.00	35.00	37.50
	Region 3	31.50	33.50	35.50
	Region 4	30.00	31.50	33.50

(a) What is the typical area of
    (i) a small pre-1920 house,
    (ii) a large house built in 1935?

(b) What is the rebuilding cost per square foot for
    (i) a small pre-1920 house in Region 1,
    (ii) a medium-sized house, built in 1950 in Region 3,
    (iii) a large house built in 1930 in Region 4?

(c) Mike Sainsbury's house was built in 1933 in Region 2. It has an area of 1100 ft^2. Estimate the total cost of rebuilding.

(d) Joyce Stradling's house was built in 1961 in Region 4. It has an area of 1700 ft^2. Estimate the total cost of rebuilding.

(e) One of the regions is London. By studying the different rates, decide which region is London.

15 A shopkeeper bought 80 boxes of strawberries at 50p each. He was forced to throw six away, but he sold the others at 75p per box. How much profit did he make?

16

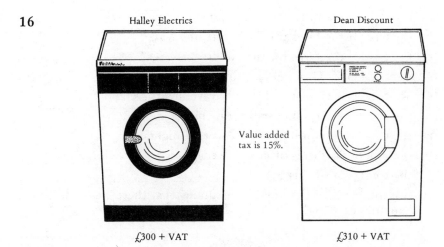

Halley Electrics   Dean Discount

Value added tax is 15%.

£300 + VAT   £310 + VAT

(a) Mrs Goode buys a washing machine from Halley Electrics. How much does she pay?

(b) Mrs Baird bought her washing machine at Dean Discount. How much more did she pay?

(c) Dean Discount offers the washing machine on hire-purchase under the following terms.

    Deposit £75 + 24 monthly payments of £13.80

What is the total hire-purchase price of the washing machine?

17 A family of five (two adults and three children) had a 14-day Continental holiday. Their costs are set out below.

Cross Channel — single fares

Passengers		Car
Adult	£24.00	£15 per metre or part of a metre
Child	half-price	

Accommodation — dinner, bed and breakfast

Adult	£16.50 per night
Child	half-price

Car

Length	4 m 85 cm
Distance travelled	800 km
Petrol consumption	10 km per litre
Cost of petrol	50p per litre

Find

(a) the cost to take the car on the ferry one way,

(b) the cost of the fares for the adults one way,

(c) the cost of the fares for the children one way,

(d) the total cross-Channel fare for a single crossing,

(e) the total cross-Channel fare for travelling there and back,

(f) the accommodation costs for one night,

(g) the total accommodation costs for 14 nights,

(h) the number of litres of petrol used,

(i) the total cost of this petrol,

(j) the total cost of the holiday, assuming that there were additional expenses of £254.

18

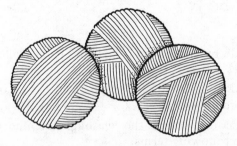

Some wool is sold in 50 g balls costing 85p each. A cardigan needs 860 g. How much will the wool cost? (Include the cost of the wool that is left over.)

19 The hire charges for electric power tools when hired from Buildahire are given below.

	Daily	Weekly
Damp proof injector	£11.00	£33.00
Paint stripper	£4.20	£8.40
Angle grinders 110/240 volts (when fitted with abrasive 9 in discs will cut concrete, stone, metal, asphalt and tiles, cutting discs sold separately)	£6.20	£14.10
Circular saws 8 in (maximum depth of cut 2 in)	£6.80	£14.40
Jigsaws	£4.20	£8.40
Nibblers	£6.00	£17.50
Electric planers	£6.00	£17.50
Small angle grinders (suitable for 4 in discs)	£3.00	£9.00
Screwdrivers (for driving screws up to 6 mm diameter)	£6.00	£14.40
Router (woodwork tool)	£7.00	£21.20
Extension leads (min. hire 1 week)		£2.20

(a) What is the cost of hiring a jigsaw for 2 days?

(b) What is the cost of hiring a router for 3 weeks?

(c) Harry needs an electric planer for 4 days. How much will it cost him? Can he keep it longer without extra charge?

(d) Olive requires a paint stripper for 10 days. What is the cheapest way she can hire it?

20 Robert Whatley's weekly car expenses are calculated as follows.

Divide the mileage for the week by 10 and add 5

This gives the number of pounds he is paid.

(a) How much is he paid if he travels 500 miles in a week?

(b) How much is he paid in a week when his mileage is 280 miles?

(c) Last week his car expenses came to £52. How many miles did he travel?

Perimeter and Area

In questions 1 to 8, find the perimeter of each of the given shapes. All measurements are in centimetres.

1

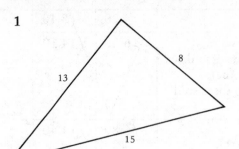

2

3

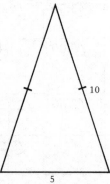

4

5

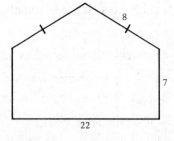

6

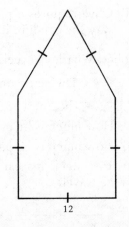

7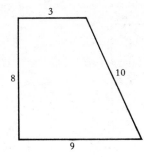

8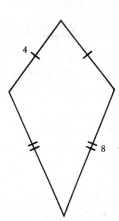

In questions 9 to 23, if the dots are spaced 1 cm apart, find
(a) the perimeter,   (b) the area.

9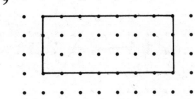

10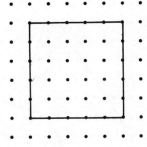

11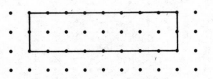

12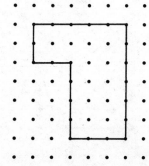

13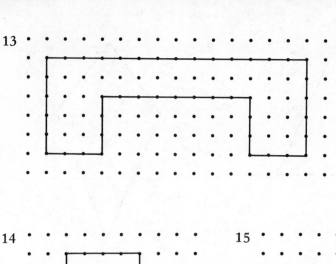

14 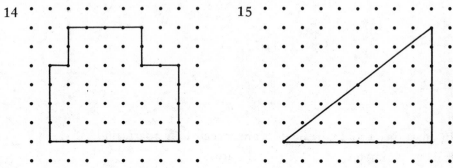 15

16 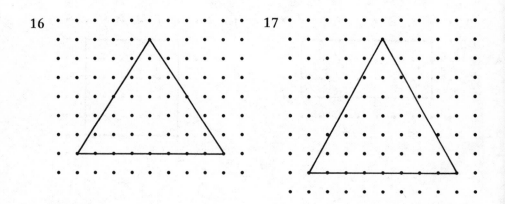 17

18 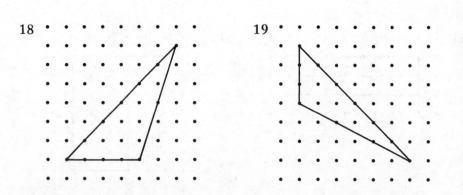 19

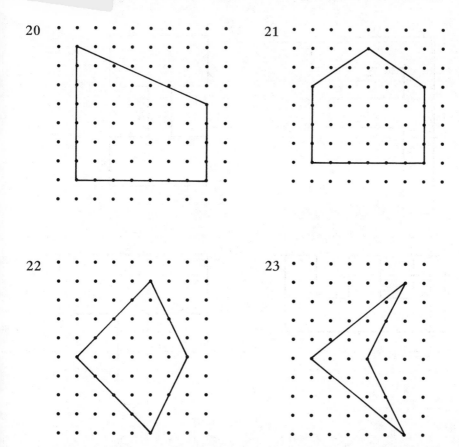

20 21

22 23

In questions 24 to 29 find, by dividing each into rectangles

(a) the perimeter of each shape,   (b) the area of each shape,

All measurements are in centimetres.

24 25

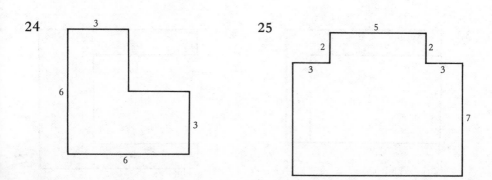

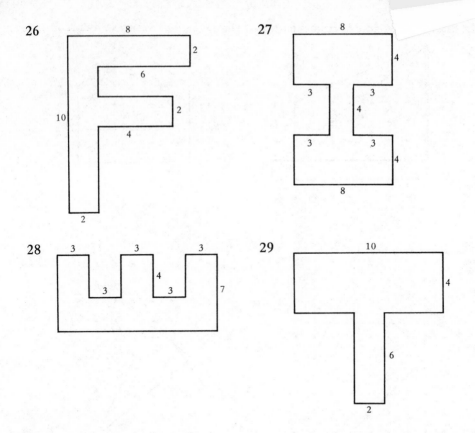

In questions 30 to 33, find the area of the shaded part. All measurements are in centimetres.

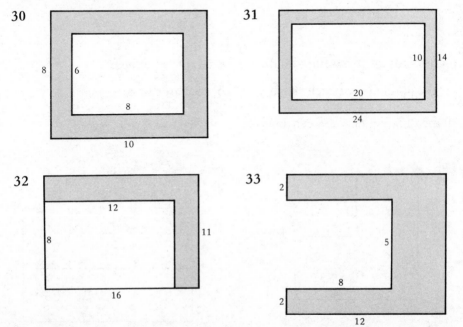

In questions 34 to 41, find the area of the triangle.

34

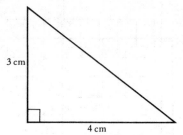

3 cm

4 cm

35

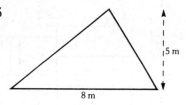

5 m

8 m

36

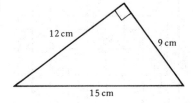

12 cm

9 cm

15 cm

37

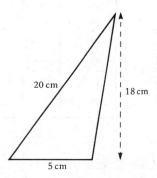

20 cm

18 cm

5 cm

38

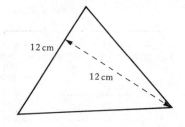

12 cm

12 cm

39

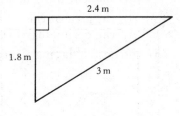

2.4 m

1.8 m

3 m

40

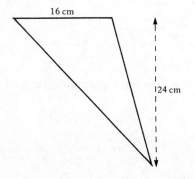

16 cm

24 cm

41

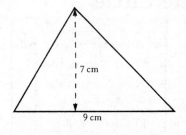

7 cm

9 cm

42   The plan shows the ground floor of a house.

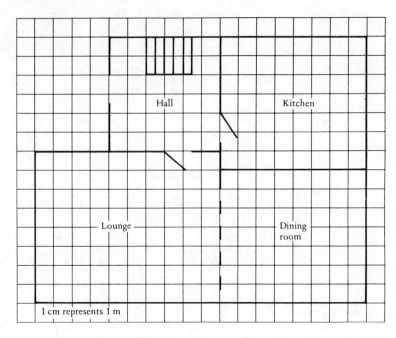

Use the plan to find
(a) (i) the length of the lounge,
     (ii) the width of the lounge,
(b) (i) the length of the kitchen,
     (ii) the width of the kitchen,
(c) (i) the area of the lounge,
     (ii) the perimeter of the kitchen,
(d) the cost of laying a carpet in the lounge at £12 per square metre.

The Circle   14

1   The diameter of a car wheel is 14 in.
    (a) What is its radius?
    (b) How far will the car move forward for each complete turn of the
         wheel?
    (Take $\pi = \frac{22}{7}$.)

2   A circular table has a diameter of 1.5 m. How far is it around the
    edge? (Take $\pi = 3.14$.)

3   The wheel of a bicycle has a diameter of 42 cm.
    (a) What is the circumference of this wheel?
    (b) How far will the bicycle move forward for one complete turn of
         each wheel?
    (Take $\pi = \frac{22}{7}$.)

4   The circumference of a circular garden pool is 44 m. What is the
    diameter of the pool? (Take $\pi = \frac{22}{7}$.)

5   Merle's bicycle wheels have a radius of 20 cm.
    (a) What is the circumference of each wheel? (Take $\pi = 3.14$.)
    (b) How far will the bicycle move forward if each wheel makes 100
         complete turns?
    (c) How many complete turns will each wheel make if Merle cycles
         1000 m?

6   How far is it around the equator of the earth? Assume that the
    equator is a circle of diameter 7930 miles. Take π to be 3.14, and
    give your answer correct to the nearest thousand miles.

7

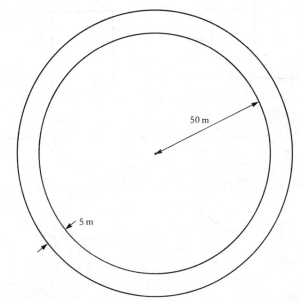

A circular running track has an inner radius of 50 m. The track is,
everywhere, 5 m wide.
(a) What is the outer radius of the track?
(b) How far is it once around the track on the inside?
(c) How far is it once around the track on the outside?
(d) Paul runs ten times around the track on the inside, while Hugh
     runs the same number of times on the outside. How much further
     does Hugh run than Paul? (Take $\pi = 3.14$.)

Solids and Containers

In questions 1 to 10, find the volume of each solid. All dimensions are in centimetres.

1
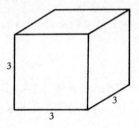

2
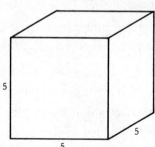

3
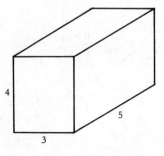

4
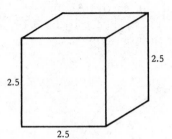

5
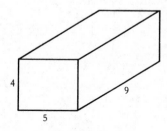

6
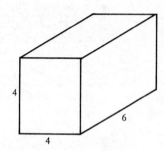

7
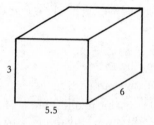

8
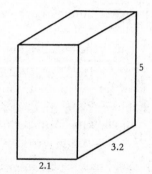

9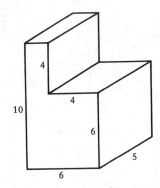

10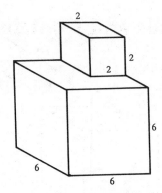

11 A rectangular cardboard box measures 30 cm × 20 cm × 20 cm. Find the capacity of this box.

12 Peter's bedroom measures 4 m × 3 m × 2.5 m. Find its volume.

13 An open rectangular tank is 30 cm long, 20 cm wide and 15 cm high. How much water will it hold
(a) in cm³, (b) in litres? (1 litre = 1000 cm³.)

14 A swimming pool is 30 m long, 15 m wide and 2.5 m deep. It is filled with water to a level 0.5 m from the top. What volume of water is in the pool?

15 Find the volume of a cube of sugar of side 0.5 in.

16 Find the volume of a box of cereal measuring 12 in by 9 in by 3 in.

17

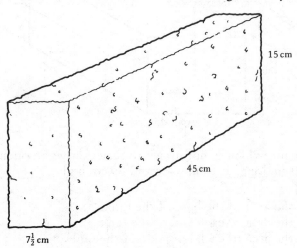

A concrete block measures 45 cm × 15 cm × 7½ cm.
(a) Find the volume of this block (i) in cm³, (ii) in m³.
    (1 m³ = 1 000 000 cm³.)
(b) How many such blocks can be made from 1 m³ of concrete?

18

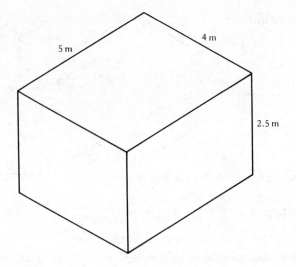

Margaret's living room is 5 m long, 4 m wide and 2.5 m high. Find
(a) the area of the floor,
(b) the area of the ceiling,
(c) the total wall area, including doors and windows,
(d) the volume of the room.

19

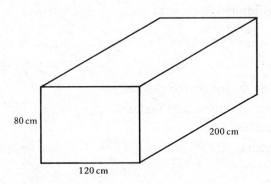

The diagram, which is not drawn to scale, shows an open rectangular tank, 200 cm long, 120 cm wide and 80 cm high.
(a) Find
      (i) the area of the base of the tank,
     (ii) the area of each end of the tank,
    (iii) the area of each long side of the tank.
(b) Use your answers to part (a) to find the total outside area of the four walls of the tank.
(c) What is the capacity of the tank, in litres?
(d) How much water is in the tank when it is three-quarters full?
(1 litre = 1000 cm³.)

20 Study this cube.

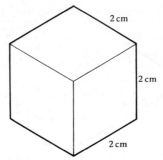

(a) How many edges does it have?
(b) How many surfaces does it have?
(c) What is the area of one face (or surface)?
(d) What is the total surface area of the cube?
(e) What is the volume of this cube?

Two similar cubes are stuck together as shown below.

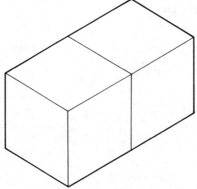

(f) What name do we give to this shape?
(g) How many (i) edges, (ii) surfaces, does it have?
(h) Find its volume.
(i) Repeat parts (f), (g) and (h) when three such cubes are stuck together, as shown in the diagram.

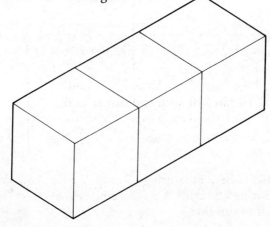

21 How many cubes are in each of the stacks given below?

(a)

(b)

(c)

(d)

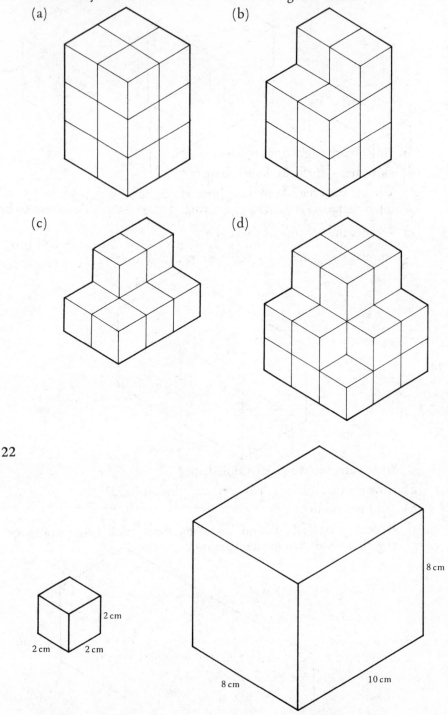

22

Plastic cubes, measuring 2 cm × 2 cm × 2 cm, are stored in a box measuring 10 cm × 8 cm × 8 cm. How many of the cubes can be stored in this box?

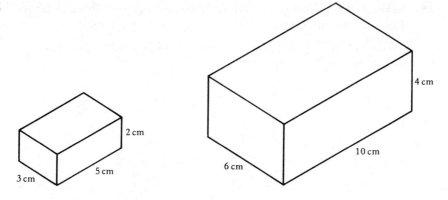

Wooden rectangular blocks measuring 5 cm X 3 cm X 2 cm are to be packed in cardboard boxes measuring 10 cm X 6 cm X 4 cm.

(a) How many wooden blocks can be packed in one cardboard box?

(b) How many cardboard boxes are needed to pack 64 wooden blocks?

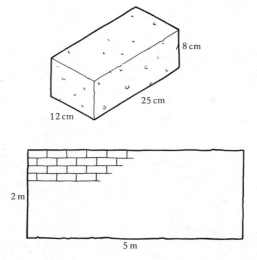

Bricks measuring 25 cm X 12 cm X 8 cm are to be used to build a wall 5 m long and 2 m high. The wall is to be 12 cm thick.

(a) Find the volume of one brick.

(b) How many bricks are laid end to end to lay the first *course* (i.e. layer of bricks) of the wall?

(c) How many courses are required to reach a height of 2 m?

(d) How many bricks are required to build the wall? (Neglect the thickness of the cement.)

25 Several shapes are given below. The broken lines show hidden edges. For each shape, write

(i) the number of edges, (ii) the number of faces,

(iii) the number of corners.

(a)

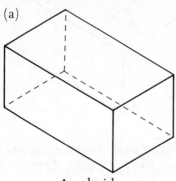

A cuboid

(b)

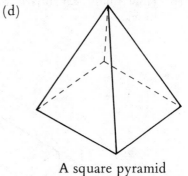

A triangular pyramid

(c)

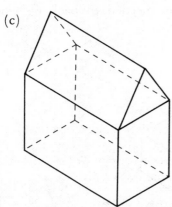

A cuboid with a prism fitting on the top

(d)

A square pyramid

(e)

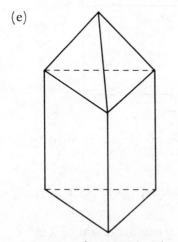

A triangular prism with a triangular pyramid

(f)

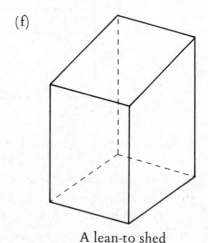

A lean-to shed

48

26

This is a container for baked beans. What mathematical name do we give to it?

27

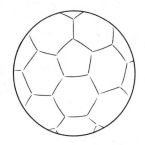

This is a football. What mathematical name do we give to it?

28

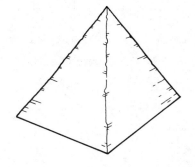

This is a paper weight that John Park brought home from a holiday in Egypt. What mathematical name do we give to it?

29

This is a book. What mathematical name do we give to this shape?

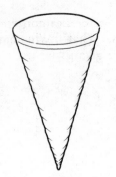

We often put ice-cream in one of these. What mathematical name do we give to the shape?

31

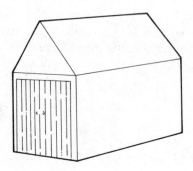

This garage can be thought of as two mathematical shapes put together. What are they?

32

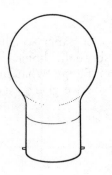

This light bulb can be thought of as two shapes. What are they?

33

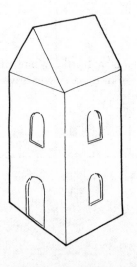

This saddle-backed church tower is made up of two simple shapes. What are they?

34 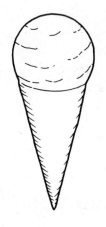 This ice-cream cornet is made up of two shapes. What are they?

Nets 16

1 The diagram below shows part of the net of an open rectangular box measuring 6 cm by 3 cm by 2 cm.

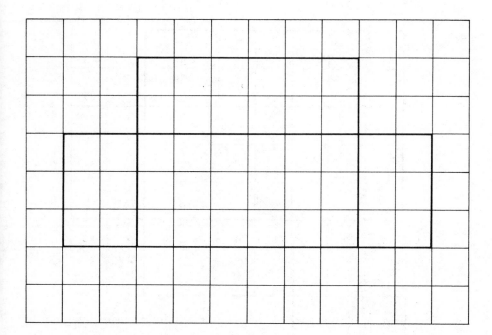

(a) Copy and complete this net.
(b) Calculate the area of card used to draw this net and, hence, to make the box.
(c) Calculate the capacity of the box, in cubic centimetres.

2

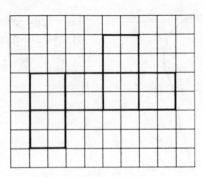

(a) What shape will this net give?

(b) How many (i) edges, (ii) corners, will the resulting shape have?

3

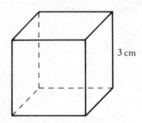

3 cm

Draw a full-size net for this cube.

4

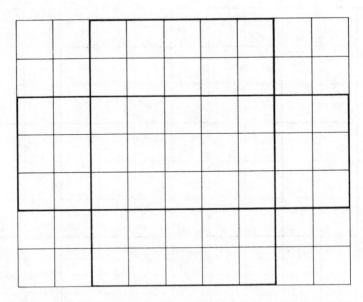

The diagram shows part of the net for a cuboid measuring 5 cm by 3 cm by 2 cm.

(a) Copy the diagram and complete the net.

(b) How many possible positions are there for the missing side? Show these positions on a sketch.

(c) Find the total surface area of this cuboid.

5   The diagram, which is drawn half size, gives the net of a cuboid
    whose base is A.

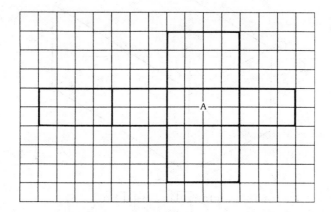

(a) Find the length, breadth and depth of this cuboid.
(b) What is the area of
     (i) the top face,
     (ii) one of the smaller side-faces?
(c) Calculate the volume of the cuboid.

6   A rectangular piece of card measures 11 cm by 9 cm. Four squares of
    sides 3 cm are cut from the corners to give a net for an open box.

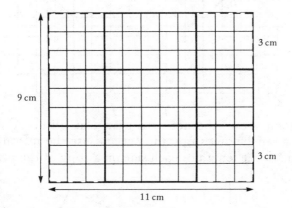

(a) What are the measurements of the box?
(b) What is the area of the original piece of card?
(c) What area is removed?
(d) What area remains to form the net?
(e) What fraction of the original card is wasted?
(f) What is the volume of the box?

7

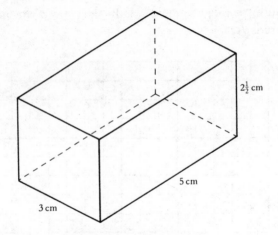

2½ cm

5 cm

3 cm

Draw a net for this rectangular closed box.

8

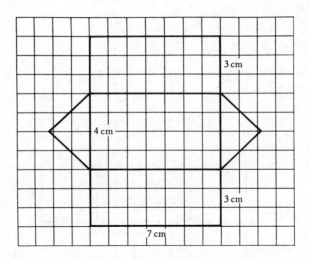

3 cm

4 cm

3 cm

7 cm

The diagram shows the net of a triangular prism. A sketch of the prism is given below. Copy the net and use the information shown on it to mark the length of each side on a copy of the prism.

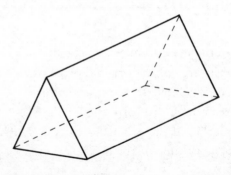

9 Draw a net for this triangular prism.

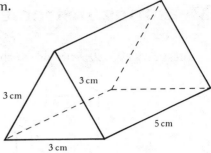

3 cm
3 cm
3 cm
5 cm

10

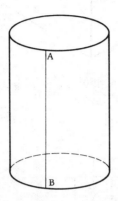

A

B

The diagram shows a mathematical shape which has been made from thin card. It is open at both ends.

(a) What name do we give to this shape?

(b) The card is cut along AB and opened out flat. Sketch a diagram to show this flat shape.

(c) The diameter of the circular base is 4 cm. Find the distance right around the base of the shape starting at B. (Use $\pi = 3.14$.)

(d) If the length of AB is 6 cm, draw an accurate full-size drawing of the flat shape.

11 The diagram shows a clown's hat.

(a) What name do we give to this shape?

(b) A cut is made along the straight line VA, and the card is opened out flat. Sketch the flat shape. What common shape is the flat shape a part of?

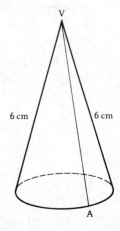

V
6 cm
6 cm
A

Measuring Instruments

In questions 1 to 26 write down the value indicated by the pointer.

1

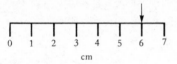

2

3

4

5

6

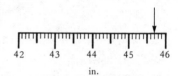

7

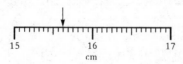

8

9

10

11

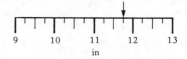

12

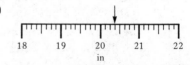

13

14

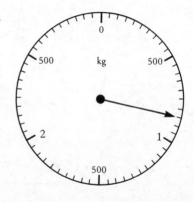

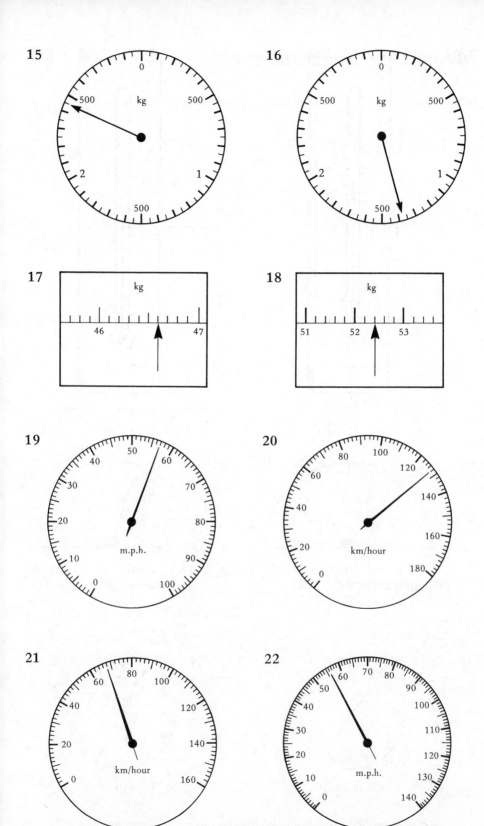

23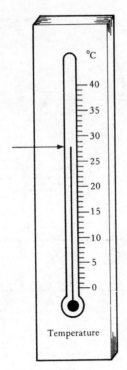

24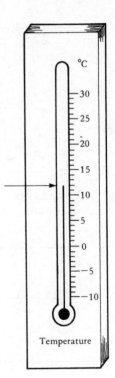

25

The petrol tank holds 12 gallons when full.

26

The petrol tank holds 60 litres when full.

27

Lesson begins

Lesson ends

How many minutes long was the lesson?

28 (a) The train is due at 5.34. How
many minutes are there before
it should arrive?

(b) The bus is due at 2005. How
many minutes are there before
it should arrive?

29 The diagram shows a thermometer marked in degrees Fahrenheit and in degrees Celsius.

(a) What Fahrenheit temperature
does the thermometer show?

(b) What Celsius temperature does
the thermometer show?

The temperature goes up by 20°C.

(c) What is the new Celsius
reading?

(d) What is the new Fahrenheit
reading?

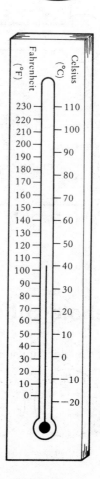

30 The thermometer shows the minimum and maximum temperatures recorded on a summer's day, in degrees Celsius.

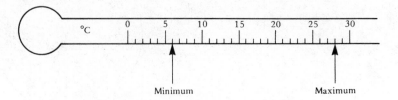

(a) What was the minimum temperature recorded?

(b) What was the maximum temperature recorded?

(c) By how many degrees did the temperature change?

31 The thermometer shows the minimum and maximum temperatures recorded on a winter's day, in degrees Celsius.

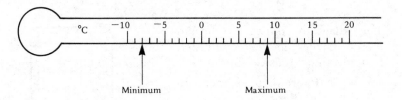

(a) What was the minimum temperature recorded?

(b) What was the maximum temperature recorded?

(c) By how many degrees did the temperature change?

Household Bills   18

1   Read the electricity meters shown below and opposite.

(a)

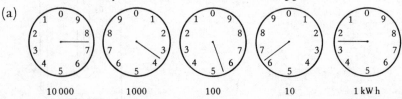

(b)

| 10 000 | 1000 | 100 | 10 | 1 kW h |

(c)

| 10 000 | 1000 | 100 | 10 | 1 kW h |

2　A meter reading on 4 April was 42 793 and on 3 July it was 43 007.

(a) How many units had been used?

(b) How much will these units cost if each unit costs 5.5 p?

3　Electricity bills are sent once a quarter. Look at the electricity bill given below and answer the questions that follow.

Northern Electricity Authority				Amount
Meter Readings				
Previous	Present			
27426	28269			
		Domestic tariff		
		☐ units at 6.00 p		☐
		Standing charge		£8.25
			Total amount due	☐

(a) What was the reading
　　(i) at the beginning of the quarter,
　　(ii) at the end of the quarter?

(b) How many units were used during the quarter?

(c) What was the cost of 1 unit of electricity?

(d) What was the cost of the number of units used?

(e) How much was the standing charge?

(f) Find the total amount due.

4   Economy 12 tariff for electricity charges 5.5 p for each unit used during the day, and 3.1 p for each unit used during the night.

(a) How much will Ted have to pay for 700 units charged at the day rate?

(b) How much will he have to pay for 450 units charged at the night rate?

(c) If there is a standing charge of £9, find the total amount of Ted's electricity bill.

5   The diagrams show the readings on Mr Watts' electricity meter on two given dates.

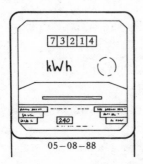 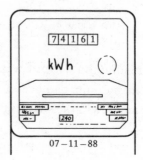

05 – 08 – 88   07 – 11 – 88

(a) In which month of the year is
   (i) the first reading taken,
   (ii) the second reading taken?

(b) How many units of electricity were used during the quarter?

(c) What is the cost of this electricity, if each unit costs 6.15 p? Give your answer correct to the nearest penny.

(d) Apart from the cost of the units used Mr Watts has to pay a fixed charge of £7.85. What is the total amount Mr Watts must pay for his electricity for the quarter?

6   Study the following electricity bill.

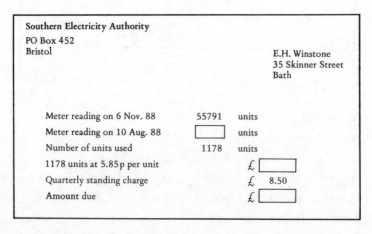

Southern Electricity Authority
PO Box 452
Bristol

E.H. Winstone
35 Skinner Street
Bath

Meter reading on 6 Nov. 88	55791	units
Meter reading on 10 Aug. 88	☐	units
Number of units used	1178	units
1178 units at 5.85 p per unit	£ ☐	
Quarterly standing charge	£ 8.50	
Amount due	£ ☐	

(a) What was the meter reading on 10 August 1988?

(b) How many units of electricity have been used?

(c) What is the total cost of these units, correct to the nearest penny?

(d) How much is the quarterly standing charge?

(e) What is the total amount due?

7   The total cost of a gas bill is given by

$$\text{Total cost} = \text{Standing charge} + \text{Cost of gas used}$$

Find

(a) the total cost when the standing charge is £8.75 and the cost of the gas used is £37.43,

(b) the cost of the gas used when the standing charge is £8.50 and the total cost is £39.50,

(c) the standing charge when the cost of the gas is £56.72 and the total cost is £64.52.

8   Last quarter Jenni Brooke used 240 therms of gas. Each therm costs 40 p.

(a) How much must she pay for the gas she has used?

(b) In addition, she must pay a standing charge of £9.50. How much is due to the Gas Board?

9   During the third quarter of last year Frank Henessey used 312 therms of gas. Each therm cost 38 p and, in addition, there was a standing charge of £10. Find the total cost of gas for the quarter.

10

Date of reading	Meter reading		Gas supplied		VAT (%)	Charges
	Present	Previous	Cubic feet (hundreds)	Therms		
05−02−88	☐	7291	347	357	0	
	Standing charge					£13.75
	Cost of 357 therms at 43p per therm					£ ☐
	Total amount due					£ ☐

Find the numbers missing from the three boxes.

11   Anne's telephone bill shows that she has used 674 units at 5.5 p per unit. How much will this cost?

12   Mr Symes' telephone bill comes to £58.60, not counting the VAT. If the rate of value added tax is 15%, how much must he pay British Telecom?

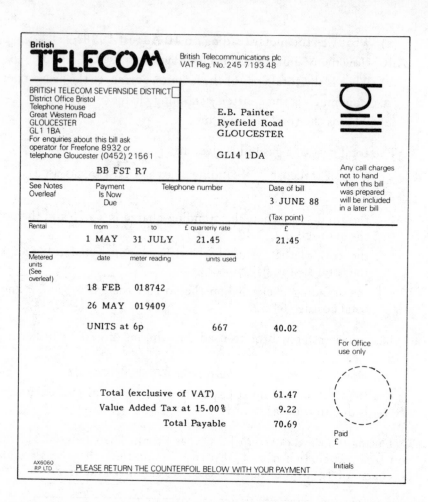

British

TELECOM

British Telecommunications plc
VAT Reg. No. 245 7193 48

BRITISH TELECOM SEVERNSIDE DISTRICT
District Office Bristol
Telephone House
Great Western Road
GLOUCESTER
GL1 1BA
For enquiries about this bill ask
operator for Freefone 8932 or
telephone Gloucester (0452) 21561

E.B. Painter
Ryefield Road
GLOUCESTER

GL14 1DA

Any call charges
not to hand
when this bill
was prepared
will be included
in a later bill

BB FST R7

See Notes Overleaf	Payment Is Now Due	Telephone number	Date of bill	
			3 JUNE 88	
			(Tax point)	

Rental	from	to	£ quarterly rate	£
	1 MAY	31 JULY	21.45	21.45

Metered units (See overleaf)	date	meter reading	units used	
	18 FEB	018742		
	26 MAY	019409		
	UNITS at 6p		667	40.02

For Office use only

Total (exclusive of VAT)   61.47
Value Added Tax at 15.00%   9.22
Total Payable   70.69

Paid
£

AX6060
RP LTD   PLEASE RETURN THE COUNTERFOIL BELOW WITH YOUR PAYMENT   Initials

(a) How much is the total rental for the quarter?

(b) What was the meter reading on (i) 18 February, (ii) 26 May?

(c) How many metered units have been used?

(d) What is the total payable before the tax is added?

(e) How much VAT is added to the bill?

(f) What is the total amount due to British Telecom?

Constructions 19

(Protractors may be used in this chapter.)

1 Construct a triangle ABC in which AB = 12 cm, AC = 11 cm and
BC = 8 cm. Draw, and measure the length of, the perpendicular
from C to AB.

2   Construct a triangle ABC in which AB = 10 cm, BC = 8 cm and AB̂C = 120°. What is the length of AC?

3   Construct a triangle PQR in which PQ = 13 cm, QP̂R = 40° and PQ̂R = 60°. Measure the length of each of the sides PR and RQ.

4   Construct a triangle XYZ in which XY = YZ = 8 cm and XŶZ = 120°. Measure
(a) the length of XZ,   (b) the size of the angle XZY.

5   Draw a quadrilateral ABCD in which AB = 8.5 cm, AD = 9.5 cm, BÂD = 90°, AD̂C = 70° and AB̂C = 75°. Measure the length of
(a) AC,   (b) BC,   (c) DC.

6   Construct the parallelogram shown in the sketch. Use it to find the length of
(a) AC,   (b) BD.

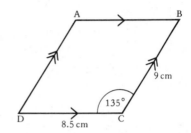

7   Draw a kite ABCD in which BD = 9 cm, AB = AD = 8.4 cm, and BC = DC = 10.5 cm. Measure and write
(a) the length of AC,
(b) the size of the angle BAD.

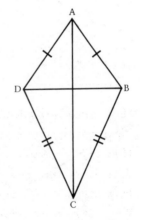

8   Use the data given in the diagram to draw ABCDE.
(a) What name do we give to this shape?

From your diagram
(b) measure the size of angle BCD.
(c) find the distance of C from AE.

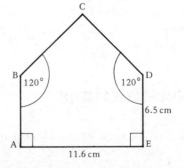

Bearings and Scale Drawings

1   For each of the following diagrams give

   (i) the bearing of A from B,

   (ii) the bearing of B from A.

(a)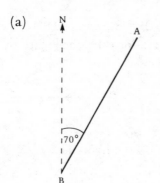

(b)

(c)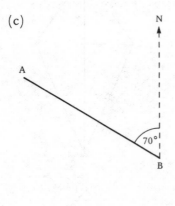

(d)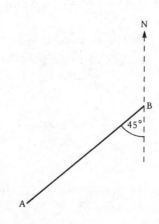

2   Draw sketches to show the directions given by each of the following three-figure bearings.

   (a) 060°   (b) 120°   (c) 300°   (d) 250°

   (e) 330°

3

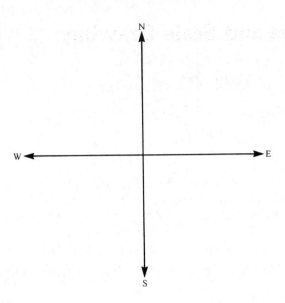

Write each of the following directions as a three-figure bearing.
(a) due west   (b) south-east   (c) north-west
(d) due south

4   Draw sketches to show the directions given by
(a) S50°E,   (b) N20°W,   (c) N75°E,   (d) S10°W.

5   Convert
(a) N34°W,   (b) S20°E,   (c) S42°W,   (d) N70°E,
into three-figure bearings.

6   The scale of the map is '1 cm represents 1 km'.
(a) What real distance is represented by a length on the map of
(i) 4 cm, (ii) 8.6 cm?
(b) What distance on the map represents an actual distance of
(i) 20 km, (ii) 75 km?

7   The scale of a map is 1 : 10 000.
(a) What real distance is represented by a length on the map of
(i) 5 cm, (ii) 9.5 cm? (Give your answers in metres.)
(b) What distance on the map represents an actual distance of
(i) 800 m, (ii) 2 km? (Give your answers in centimetres.)

8

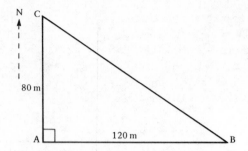

Two of Alison's friends are called Brenda and Cathy. The diagram shows that Brenda's home is 120 m due east of Alison's and Cathy's home is 80 m due north of Alison's. Make a scale drawing using 1 cm to represent 10 m. Use your drawing to find

(a) how far it is from Cathy's home to Brenda's,

(b) the three-figure bearing of Brenda's home from Cathy's.

9

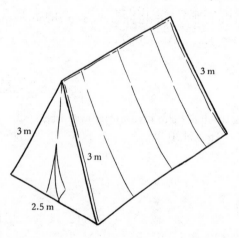

The end wall of a ridge tent is a triangle. The base is 2.5 m and the sloping edges are each 3 m. Make a scale drawing of the end wall using a scale of 1 cm to $\frac{1}{2}$ m. Use your drawing to find the height of the tent.

10 From a point, A, on the ground which is 240 m from the base of the Eiffel Tower, the angle of elevation of the top is 51°. Use 1 cm to represent 20 m and make a scale drawing. Hence, find the height of the tower.

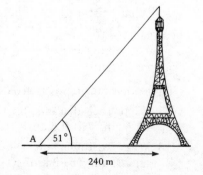

11 From the top of a church tower, 200 ft high, the angle of depression of a house is 30°. Use 1 cm to represent 20 ft and make a scale drawing. How far is the house from the foot of the tower?

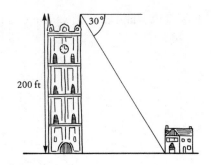

200 ft

12 From a point on the ground 200 ft away from the bottom of Nelson's Column, in Trafalgar Square, the angle of elevation of the top is 39°. Use 1 cm to represent 20 ft and make a scale drawing. How high is Nelson's Column?

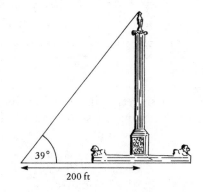

39°

200 ft

13

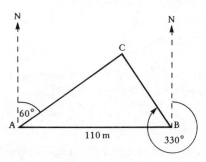

ABC represents a triangular field. B is 110 m due east of A, C is on a bearing of 060° from A, and C is on a bearing of 330° from B. Make a scale drawing of this field using 1 cm to represent 10 m. Use your diagram to find

(a) the distance of C from A,

(b) the distance of C from B,

(c) the three-figure bearing of A from B,

(d) the three-figure bearing of B from C.

14   The diagram shows the positions of three villages, P, Q and R.

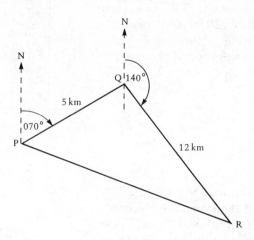

Using the distances and bearings shown on the diagram, make a scale drawing to show the positions of the three villages. Use a scale of 1 cm to represent 1 km.

(a) Measure PR, to the nearest millimetre, and hence find the distance between villages P and R (correct to the nearest tenth of a kilometre).

(b) Measure angle QPR, and hence find
   (i) the bearing of R from P,
   (ii) the bearing of P from R.

15   Use the outline map opposite to answer the following questions. The scale of the map is 1 cm represents 50 km.

(a) Which Welsh city is due west of London?

(b) Which Scottish city is almost due north of Gloucester?

(c) Which city is almost due east of Liverpool?

(d) What is the distance and bearing of Manchester from Exeter?

(e) What is the distance and bearing of Edinburgh from London?

(f) Which town is approximately 100 km on a bearing of 110° from London?

(g) Which city is approximately 150 km on a bearing of 285° from London?

(h) Which city is approximately 225 km in a direction S20°W of Manchester?

(i) Which city is approximately 330 km in a direction N32°W of Brighton?

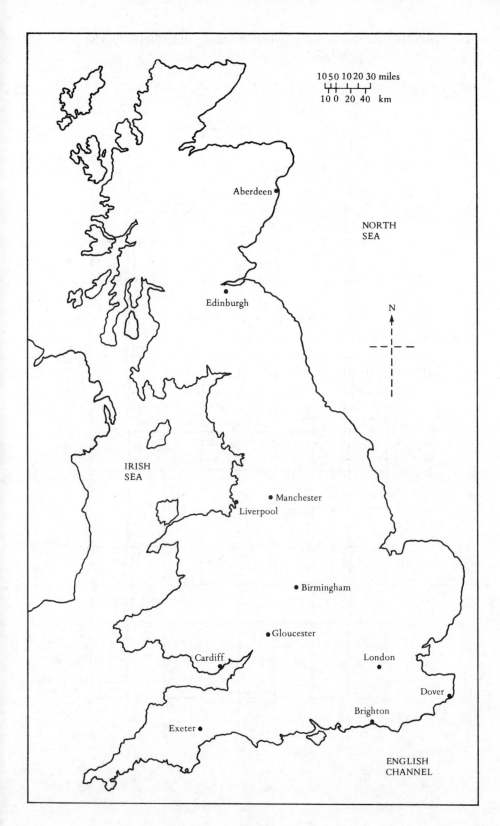

10 5 0 10 20 30 miles
10 0 20 40 km

NORTH
SEA

N

Aberdeen

Edinburgh

IRISH
SEA

Manchester
Liverpool

Birmingham

Gloucester

Cardiff

London

Dover

Brighton

Exeter

ENGLISH
CHANNEL

71

16 Given below is a scale drawing of the ground floor of a house. Each square of the grid has a side of 1 cm and represents 1 m.

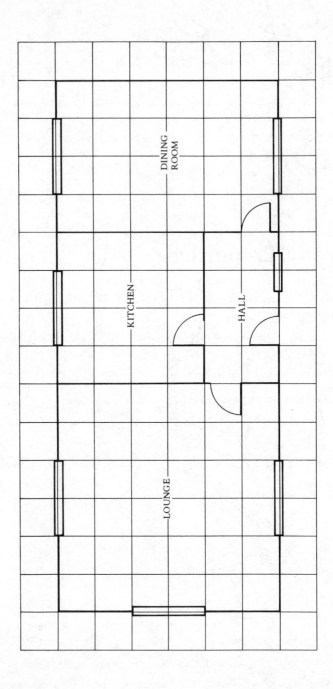

(a) Measure the diagram and then copy and complete the table.

Room	Length (m)	Width (m)	Area (m²)
Lounge			
Kitchen			
Dining room			
Hall			

(b) How much will it cost to lay a carpet in the lounge, if the price of the carpet is £15 per square metre and it is fitted free?

(c) The cost of the carpet in the dining room is £240. How much is this per square metre?

Ratio and Proportion 21

1   In Rob's class there are 12 boys and 18 girls. What is the ratio of boys to girls?

2   On a shelf there are 24 red books and 32 green books. What is the ratio of

(a) red books to green books,   (b) green books to red books?

3   Clear Fresh toothpaste is sold in three sizes.

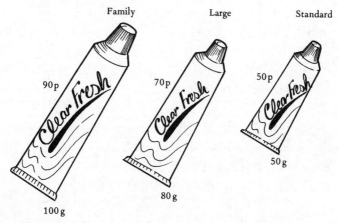

What is the ratio of

(a) the cost of the family size to the cost of the standard size,
(b) the cost of the large size to the cost of the family size,
(c) the mass of the large size to the mass of the standard size,
(d) the mass of the standard size to the mass of the family size?

73

4   A recipe for 15 rich cakes includes 100 g of sugar and 200 g of flour.
   (a) How much of each ingredient would be needed to make 30 of these?
   (b) If 600 g of flour is used, how many cakes would you expect?
   (c) Sugar costs 50 p a kilogram. How much would the sugar for 45 cakes cost?

5   A recipe for a pizza to serve 4 people, includes 145 g of plain flour, 90 millilitres of milk and 115 g of tinned tomatoes. How much of each ingredient would be required to make a pizza to serve
   (a) 8 people,   (b) 12 people?

6   A recipe for 24 Welsh cakes includes 200 g of flour, 80 g of margarine and 100 g of sugar.
   (a) How much of each ingredient is required to make 36 Welsh cakes?
   (b) How much of each ingredient is required to make 18 Welsh cakes?
   (c) If 1 kg of flour costs 35 p, how much will the flour for 24 Welsh cakes cost?

7   The total amount of money raised at the Spring School Fayre was £1029. This money was divided between the school and a local charity in the ratio 5:2, respectively. How much did the local charity receive?

8   The ratio of the length of a room to its width is 4:3. The room is 6 yd long.
   (a) How wide is it?
   (b) What is the area of the room?

9   An off-licence sells five bottles of wine to every two bottles of spirits. One week they sold 176 bottles of spirits.
   (a) How many bottles of wine did they sell?
   (b) How many bottles did they sell altogether?

10 A recipe for 16 flapjacks includes 4 oz of margarine and 6 oz of rolled oats.
   (a) How much of each ingredient would be required to make 48 flapjacks?
   (b) Margarine costs 64 p per pound. How much would the margarine for 16 flapjacks cost?

11 A recipe for making 15 nutty drops includes 50 g of mixed nuts and 125 g of plain flour.

(a) How much of each ingredient is needed to make 60 nutty drops?

(b) How much of each ingredient is needed to make 3 nutty drops?

(c) Flour costs 36 p a kilogram. How much does the flour for 15 nutty drops cost?

12 A recipe for macaroni cheese sauce to serve eight gives the following ingredients.

> 40 g flour
> 40 g margarine
> 200 g cheese
> 600 millilitres milk

Write out the quantities of each ingredient to make this sauce for

(a) four people, (b) six people.

13 A car travels 45 miles on 1 gallon of petrol.

(a) How far will it travel on 5 gallons of petrol?

(b) How many gallons are needed to travel 315 miles?

14 A lorry travels 100 km on 20 litres of diesel.

(a) How far will this lorry travel on 55 litres of diesel?

(b) How many litres of diesel are required for the lorry to travel 550 km?

15 Lisa earns £22 in 4 hours. How much will she earn in

(a) 1 hour, (b) 36 hours?

16 3 m of material costs £8.10. How much will 7 m of the same material cost?

17 In the school hall, there are 30 rows of chairs. Each row has 12 chairs.

(a) How many chairs are there?

(b) If the same number of chairs is arranged in 24 rows, how many chairs will there be in each row?

(c) If there must be 18 chairs in each row, how many rows will there be?

18 The scale of a map is 1 : 10 000.

(a) What distance, in metres, does 12 cm on the map represent?

(b) What distance on the map represents a distance of 2.5 km?

19 The scale used to make a model of a railway engine is 1 : 72.

    (a) If the engine is 7.2 m long, how long is the model?

    (b) If one wheel of the model has a diameter of 1.5 cm, find, in metres, the diameter of the corresponding wheel on the engine.

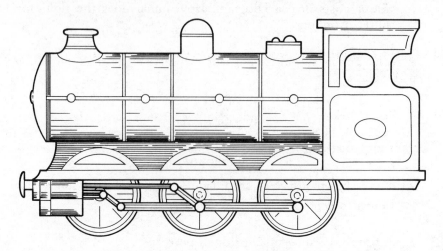

20 The scale on the plan of a building is 1 : 250.

    (a) How many metres does 4 cm represent?

    (b) On the plan, a workshop measures 16 cm by 12 cm. What are the dimensions of the actual workshop?

21 Joan and Jane are sisters. They each draw a plan of their lounge.

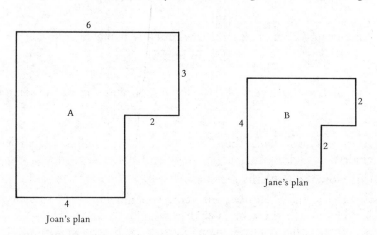

    (a) Work out the scale factor from A to B.

    (b) Copy both diagrams and fill in the missing lengths.

    (c) In diagram A the scale is 1 cm ≡ 1 m. What is the scale in diagram B?

    (d) Find the area, in square metres, of their lounge.

22 The scale of an Ordnance Survey map is 1 : 50 000.

    (a) What distance, in metres, does 1 cm on the map represent?

    (b) What distance, in kilometres, does 10 cm on the map represent?

    (c) Two villages are 10 km apart. How far apart will they be on the map?

23 Two towns are 2 km apart. On a map they are 8 cm apart. What is the scale of the map, in the form 1:n?

24 A shirt, marked £20, is reduced to £15 in a sale. Another shirt is marked £24. How much will it cost in the sale, if it is reduced in the same ratio as the price of the first shirt?

25

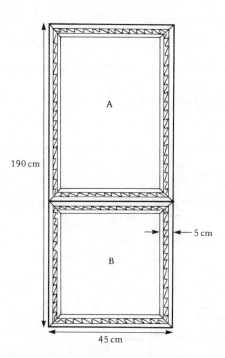

A wardrobe door is 190 cm high and 45 cm wide. Mouldings 5 cm wide are placed on the door, as shown in the diagram, to decorate it.

(a) How wide are the panels A and B?

(b) What is the height of panel A plus the height of panel B?

(c) If the ratio of the height of panel A to the height of panel B is 3 : 2, find the height of
    (i) panel A,   (ii) panel B.

	January	February	March	April
Sunday	1 8 15 22 29	5 12 19 26	5 12 19 26	2 9 16 23 30
Monday	2 9 16 23 30	6 13 20 27	6 13 20 27	3 10 17 24
Tuesday	3 10 17 24 31	7 14 21 28	7 14 21 28	4 11 18 25
Wednesday	4 11 18 25	1 8 15 22	1 8 15 22 29	5 12 19 26
Thursday	5 12 19 26	2 9 16 23	2 9 16 23 30	6 13 20 27
Friday	6 13 20 27	3 10 17 24	3 10 17 24 31	7 14 21 28
Saturday	7 14 21 28	4 11 18 25	4 11 18 25	1 8 15 22 29

	May	June	July	August
Sunday	7 14 21 28	4 11 18 25	2 9 16 23 30	6 13 20 27
Monday	1 8 15 22 29	5 12 19 26	3 10 17 24 31	7 14 21 28
Tuesday	2 9 16 23 30	6 13 20 27	4 11 18 25	1 8 15 22 29
Wednesday	3 10 17 24 31	7 14 21 28	5 12 19 26	2 9 16 23 30
Thursday	4 11 18 25	1 8 15 22 29	6 13 20 27	3 10 17 24 31
Friday	5 12 19 26	2 9 16 23 30	7 14 21 28	4 11 18 25
Saturday	6 13 20 27	3 10 17 24	1 8 15 22 29	5 12 19 26

	September	October	November	December
Sunday	3 10 17 24	1 8 15 22 29	5 12 19 26	3 10 17 24 31
Monday	4 11 18 25	2 9 16 23 30	6 13 20 27	4 11 18 25
Tuesday	5 12 19 26	3 10 17 24 31	7 14 21 28	5 12 19 26
Wednesday	6 13 20 27	4 11 18 25	1 8 15 22 29	6 13 20 27
Thursday	7 14 21 28	5 12 19 26	2 9 16 23 30	7 14 21 28
Friday	1 8 15 22 29	6 13 20 27	3 10 17 24	1 8 15 22 29
Saturday	2 9 16 23 30	7 14 21 28	4 11 18 25	2 9 16 23 30

Study the calendar.

1 How many days are there
  (a) in the month of July,
  (b) in the month of December?

2 (a) How many days are there in February?
  (b) Could this be a calendar for a leap year?

3 Which month is
  (a) two months before June,
  (b) five months after May,
  (c) nine months before November?

4 How many weekends are there from
  (a) 1 May to 1 June,
  (b) 1 September to 1 December?

5 How many Mondays are there
  (a) in April,
  (b) in October?

6   How many Tuesdays are there in the first three months of the year?

7   How many Fridays are there in the last four months of the year?

8   Today is 19 September.
    (a) What day of the week is it?
    (b) What was the date last Wednesday?

9   Yesterday it was 17 May. What was the date
    (a) last Thursday,
    (b) a week last Tuesday?

10   Tomorrow it will be 26 April.
    (a) What was the date yesterday?
    (b) What will be the date a week tomorrow?

11   Tania leaves on 15 August for a ten-night holiday. On what date does she return?

12   Jim goes for a 14-night holiday on 6 July. What date does he return?

13   Elspeth goes on holiday on 8 June and returns on 21 June. How many nights is she away?

14   Peter goes on holiday on 28 July and returns on 8 August. How many nights is he away?

15   George's school closes on 19 July and reopens after the summer holiday on 5 September. How many days summer holiday does George have?

16   David starts work on 1 September. He gets paid on the twentieth of each month. How many times does he get paid before Christmas?

17   Jean goes for karate lessons every Tuesday lunchtime when school is open. The spring term starts on 4 January and ends on 7 April. School is closed for one week at half-term. How many karate lessons does Jean get during the spring term?

18   Gary's summer term starts on 11 April and ends on 20 July. Half-term is the week beginning 22 May.
    (a) How many Mondays should Gary be in school?
    (b) How many days should Gary be in school?
    (c) Geography homework is set on a Thursday and collected on the following Tuesday. It is not set over a holiday. How many Geography homeworks should Gary get during the term?

Time

1 How many hours are there
(a) from 8 a.m. to 1 p.m.,
(b) from 8 a.m. to 8 p.m.,
(c) from 8 p.m. to 8 a.m. the next day?

2 How long is it
(a) from 9.15 to 10.00,
(b) from 8.15 to 9.45,
(c) from 11.18 to 12.42?

3 (a) A 35-minute lesson starts at 10.10 a.m. At what time should it end?
(b) A 40-minute lesson ended at 3.35 p.m. At what time did it start?

4 Judi leaves home at 7.35 a.m. to drive to London. She arrives at 10.50 a.m. How long does the journey take?

5 Ian leaves home at 2.30 p.m. to travel to Manchester. The journey takes 3 hours 20 minutes. What time does he arrive?

6 Chris arrived in work at 8.38 a.m. after a 40-minute journey from home. What time did she leave home?

7

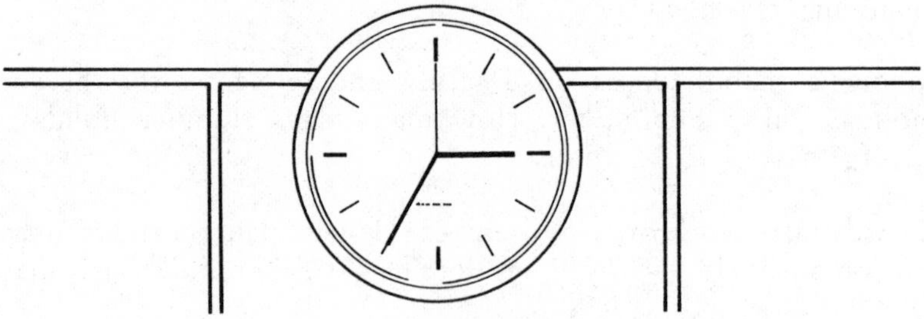

School starts at 8.45 a.m. and finishes at 3.35 p.m. The lunch break is from 11.45 a.m. to 1.00 p.m.
(a) It takes Carlo 20 minutes to walk to school. What is the latest time he can leave home to arrive in school on time?
(b) The first lesson starts at 9.10 a.m. and lasts 70 minutes. At what time does it end?
(c) How long is the lunch break?
(d) How long is morning school?
(e) How long is afternoon school?
(f) Carlo takes the same time to walk home as to walk to school. He stays in school for lunch. How long is he away from home during a normal school day?

8 Britt got in from school at twenty to five and looked at the Channel 4 programmes.

```
  4.30 COUNTDOWN
  5.00 MISTER ED
  5.30 SOLID SOUL
  6.00 REVID
  6.15 THE CHART SHOW
  7.00 CHANNEL 4 NEWS
  7.50 BOOK CHOICE
  8.00 WHAT THE PAPERS SAY
       Freelance Peter McHackay
  9.00 TANDOORI NIGHTS
  9.30 A HOUSEFUL OF PLANTS
       Blue Peter for the Bromeliad
       set
 10.00 THE GOLDEN GIRLS
       Nancy Walker guests as
       Sophia's sister in the best
       show currently on television
 10.30 THE LAST RESORT WITH
       JONATHAN ROSS
```

(a) How much of Countdown had she missed?

(b) How long did she have to wait for Solid Soul to start?

(c) How long was the programme Tandoori Nights?

(d) How long was it from the end of Book Choice to the beginning of The Golden Girls?

(e) What was on half an hour after Revid had finished?

9 The following is an extract from the BBC2 programmes one evening.

```
  6.00 FILM
       Tarzan the Magnificent
  7.25 TRANSIT
  8.00 FACE THE MUSIC
  8.30 GARDENER'S WORLD
  9.00 CITYLIGHTS
  9.30 ACTING WITH MICHAEL CAINE
 10.30 NEWSNIGHT
 11.15 WEATHERVIEW
 11.20 THE EUROPEAN SHOW JUMPING
       CHAMPIONSHIP
 12.00 FILM
       Stranger on the Third Floor
  1.05 CLOSE
```

(a) Which film is the longer and by how much?

(b) Which programme lasts exactly 1 hour?

(c) How long did Newsnight last?

(d) How much longer is Transit than Gardener's World?

(e) Because of a special news item, Citylights started at 9.06. How long was the special news item?

(f) Kriss Emmett sat down to watch television as the Tarzan film was finishing, and switched off when Newsnight was about to start. For how long did he watch television?

10   What time on the 24-hour clock corresponds to
(a) 6 a.m.,   (b) 10 p.m.,   (c) 4.30 p.m.   (d) 11.15 a.m.?

11   Judi gets up at 0645 and goes to bed at 2230. For how long is she up?

12   Give the following times in a.m./p.m. times.
(a) 0942   (b) 1942   (c) 2115   (d) 1015

13   The timetable refers to the two buses that travel from Daxton to Peckley.

Daxton – Peckley		
Daxton	0734	1148
Edgehill	0746	1200
Gormer	0802	1216
Jenner	0821	1235
Keytown	0834	1248
Peckley	0906	1320

(a) Which bus makes the faster journey between Daxton and Peckley?

(b) How long does each bus take to travel from Edgehill to Gormer?

(c) Ken lives in Jenner. It takes him 5 minutes to walk to the bus stop. What time must he leave home to catch the 1148 bus from Daxton? What time should he arrive in Peckley?

14   One day last summer, sunrise was at 0647 and sunset was at 1926. How long was the Sun up?

15   One day last winter, lighting-up time began at 1623 and ended at 0721 the next day. How long did lighting-up time last that night?

16   The table gives information about a motor racing circuit. It gives the times taken to complete different numbers of laps for different average speeds.

Average speed in miles per hour (m.p.h.)	Time taken for				
	one lap	two laps	three laps	four laps	five laps
110	2 min 4 s	4 min 8 s	6 min 12 s	8 min 16 s	10 min 20 s
112	2 min 2 s	4 min 4 s	6 min 6 s		10 min 10 s
114	2 min	4 min	6 min	8 min	10 min
116	1 min 58 s	3 min 56 s		7 min 52 s	

(a) How long does it take to do three laps at an average speed of 112 m.p.h.?

(b) How long does it take to do five laps at an average speed of 110 m.p.h.?

(c) How long does it take to do four laps at an average speed of 112 m.p.h.?

(d) How long does it take to do
(i) three laps, (ii) five laps, at an average speed of 116 m.p.h.?

(e) How long does it take to do ten laps at an average speed of
(i) 112 m.p.h., (ii) 116 m.p.h.?

(f) Estimate the time taken for one lap when the average speed is 118 m.p.h.

(g) Express the time taken for one lap at an average speed of 110 m.p.h.
(i) in minutes, (ii) in hours.

(Give each answer correct to three decimal places.)

(h) Use your answer to part (g) (ii) to find, correct to one decimal place, the length of the circuit in miles.

Holidays and Travel   24

1

Distances are in miles.

(a) What is the distance between
(i) Exeter and Bath,
(ii) Bournemouth and Southampton?

(b) The circuit for a cycle race is from Bath to Bristol, on to Exeter and then straight back to Bath. What is the total length of the circuit?

(c) A cyclist took exactly 8 hours to complete the race. What was his average speed?

2   This chart shows the distances between six places, in miles.

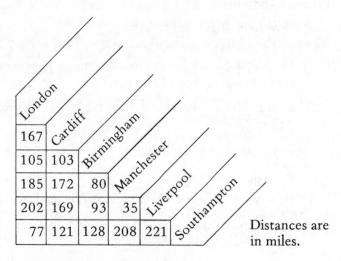

Distances are in miles.

(a) Which two places are nearest together?
(b) Which two places are furthest apart?
(c) How far is it from London to Manchester?
(d) How far is it from Liverpool to Cardiff?
(e) A car travels from Manchester to Southampton in 4 hours. What is its average speed?
(f) A lorry travels from Birmingham to Manchester at an average speed of 40 m.p.h. How long does the journey take?
(g) Tony drives from Manchester to Cardiff, then from Cardiff to Southampton, and finally returns to Manchester. How far has he driven?

3   This chart shows the distances, in kilometres, between several places in the United Kingdom.

	London	Aberdeen	Brighton	Exeter	Liverpool	Manchester
Aberdeen	806					
Brighton	89	895				
Exeter	275	911	275			
Liverpool	330	538	418	385		
Manchester	309	534	398	389	55	
Worcester	183	689	270	217	169	164

Distances are in kilometres.

(a) Which two places are nearest together?
(b) Which two places are furthest apart?
(c) How far is it from London to Exeter?
(d) How far is it from Liverpool to Aberdeen?
(e) A car travels from London to Liverpool in 5 hours. What is its average speed?
(f) A heavy lorry averages 45 km/hour for the journey from Brighton to Worcester. How long does the journey take?
(g) How far is the journey from Brighton to London, London to Manchester, then back to Brighton?

4 Donna and Steve are planning a holiday in Majorca. The prices per person in one brochure are given below.

	Hotel	Millor			Cala			Petro		
	Nights	7	10	14	7	10	14	7	10	14
DEPARTURES ON OR BETWEEN	1 May–14 May	94	103	115	109	124	144	108	123	143
	15 May–28 May	123	134	147	138	155	176	137	154	175
	29 May–4 June	117	132	144	132	153	173	131	152	172
	5 June–18 June	131	143	158	146	164	187	145	163	186
	19 June–2 July	141	158	176	156	179	205	155	178	204
	3 July–16 July	160	181	200	175	202	229	174	201	228
	17 July–23 July	188	211	231	203	232	260	202	231	259
	24 July–16 Aug.	190	219	243	205	240	272	204	239	271
	17 Aug.–23 Aug.	184	209	229	199	230	258	198	229	257
	24 Aug.–31 Aug.	181	198	223	196	219	252	195	218	251
	1 Sept.–13 Sept.	179	196	221	194	217	250	193	216	249
	14 Sept.–30 Sept.	157	184	199	172	205	228	171	204	227
	1 Oct.–31 Oct.	146	160	172	161	181	201	160	180	200

Prices are in pounds sterling (£).

(a) Which hotel gives the cheapest 10-day holiday if they leave on 1 July?
(b) What will they each have to pay if they go for
  (i) a 10-night holiday at the Hotel Cala leaving on 10 August,
  (ii) a 14-night holiday at the Hotel Petro leaving on 15 September,
  (iii) a 7-night holiday at the Hotel Millor leaving on 20 May?
(c) They have a total of £700 to spend on a holiday, and decide they need £150 of this as spending money. Can they afford to go to the Hotel Cala for 14 nights, leaving on 17 August?

5 Larry and Kate want to go to stay at the Hotel Kos, in Greece, next summer. The costs per person of the different board arrangements are given below.

	Board arrangement	Room only		B and B		Half-board		Full-board	
DEPARTURES ON OR BEFORE	No. of nights	7	14	7	14	7	14	7	14
	1 May–7 May	128	149	130	154	146	168	189	235
	8 May–14 May	130	151	132	156	154	176	192	238
	15 May–25 May	155	176	157	181	156	178	217	263
	26 May–4 June	157	178	159	183	181	203	219	266
	5 June–25 June	169	190	171	195	191	213	227	273
	26 June–9 July	179	200	181	205	200	222	235	281
	10 July–16 July	194	215	196	220	219	241	251	297
	17 July–9 Aug.	229	250	231	255	229	251	277	323
	10 Aug.–23 Aug.	219	240	221	245	261	283	273	319
	24 Aug.–31 Aug.	215	236	217	241	252	274	268	314
	1 Sept.–30 Sept.	196	217	198	222	248	270	255	299
	1 Oct.–24 Oct.	184	205	186	210	232	254	235	279

Prices are in pounds sterling (£).

(a) How much will it cost them for 14 nights bed and breakfast, if they leave on
(i) 25 May, (ii) 25 August?

(b) How much will 7 nights full-board cost them, if they leave on 19 July?

(c) How much will 14 nights half-board cost them, if they leave on 4 September?

(d) How much will the room only cost them, if they leave on 12 July for 7 nights?

(e) They have £500 to spend on board arrangements. When can they leave if they want 14 nights on half-board?

(f) How much more will 14 nights on full-board cost them than 14 nights on bed and breakfast, if they leave on 28 June?

6 The graph can be used to convert pounds sterling (£) into French francs.

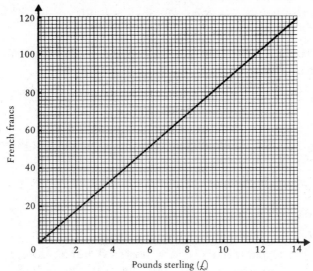

Use your graph to change

(a) £8 into francs, (b) 100 francs into pounds.

Hence find

(c) 800 francs in pounds, (d) £600 in francs.

7 The graph given below can be used to convert pounds sterling (£) into Austrian schillings. Use the graph to answer the questions that follow.

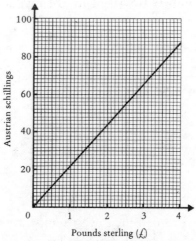

(a) Change £3.20 into Austrian schillings.
(b) How much in pounds sterling should I get for 66 schillings?
(c) How many schillings are equivalent to £4?
(d) Hence calculate the value of £1 in schillings.

8 An American tourist receives 70p for $1. How many pounds will she receive for

(a) $10,   (b) $70,   (c) $500?

9 A British tourist receives 190 pesetas for £1. How many pesetas will he receive for

(a) £50,   (b) £200,   (c) £175?

10 A British tourist returns from Spain with 900 pesetas. The bank gives him £1 for each 200 pesetas. How much will he get in pence?

11 Find which is cheaper – a jumper bought in France for 180 francs or one bought in Spain for 4200 pesetas. £1 is equivalent to 9 francs and to 190 pesetas.

12 It costs 40 pesetas to send a postcard home from Spain. If £1 is equivalent to 200 pesetas, find the cost of sending nine postcards home

(a) in pesetas,   (b) in pence.

13 The same English newspaper costs 40p in England but 240 pesetas in Spain. If £1 is equivalent to 200 pesetas, how many newspapers can be bought in England for the price of one newspaper in Spain?

14 The table shows the maximum and minimum temperatures recorded one week at five holiday resorts.

Resort	Maximum temperature (in °C)	Minimum temperature (in °C)
Bournemouth	15	2
Skegness	6	−6
St David's	8	−2
Blackpool	10	−5
Douglas	13	−3

(a) Which resort recorded the lowest temperature?
(b) Which resort recorded the highest temperature?
(c) What is the difference between Blackpool's highest and lowest temperatures?
(d) Which resort has the smallest range of temperatures?
(e) Which resort has the greatest range of temperatures?

15 A motorist leaving Laxton has a choice of routes to take for Stow.
These are shown on the map.

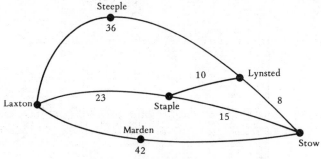

Distances are in kilometres

(a) How many different routes are there? Do not count routes that
drive away from Stow.

(b) Write down the distance from Laxton to Stow using each route.

(c) Which route is
(i) the longest, (ii) the most direct?

Straight–Line and Curved Graphs   25

1 The graph represents a train journey from a town A to a town B and
back to A, the distance between the towns being 80 km. Use the
graph to find

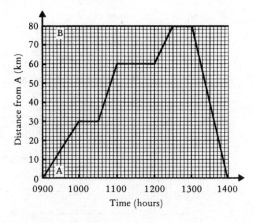

(a) the total time the train was at rest,

(b) the speed of the train for the first hour,

(c) the speed of the train on the return journey from B to A.

89

2

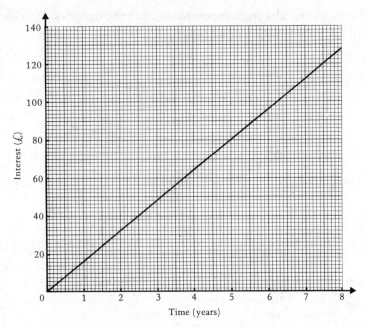

The graph shows the simple interest received when £200 is invested for a number of years at 8% per annum. Use the graph to find

(a) the simple interest received when £200 is invested for $6\frac{1}{2}$ years at 8% per annum.

(b) the number of years £200 would have to be invested at 8% per annum to receive £56 interest,

(c) the simple interest received on £600 invested for 4 years at 8% per annum.

3 Chastons Motors hire out cars. The graph shows their hire charges.

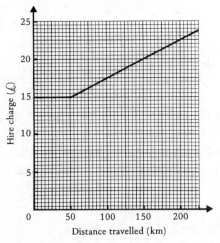

(a) What is the hire charge for a car for
(i) 100 km, (ii) 200 km?

(b) Does the charge increase steadily as the distance increases?

(c) What distance is travelled if the hire charge is £20?

West End Car Rentals also hire out cars. Some of their charges are given in the table below.

Distance travelled (km)	50	125	175
Hire charge (£)	12.50	20	25

(d) Copy the graph given for Chastons Motors on squared paper, and then plot the points representing the hire charges for West End Car Rentals. Join them with a straight line.

(e) For what distance do the two companies have the same hire charge?

4   The graph shows Sarah's journey from home to the office. She walked to the bus stop, waited, then caught the bus which dropped her outside the office.

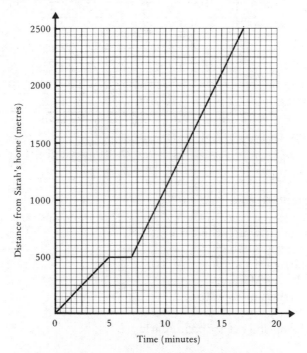

(a) How long did she take to walk to the bus stop?

(b) How long did she wait before the bus came?

(c) How many minutes did she travel on the bus?

(d) How far was the office from her home
    (i) in metres, (ii) in kilometres?

(e) How far was she from home after 9 minutes?

(f) How long had her journey taken when she was still 1.5 km from the office?

5   The graph shows the journey by car from Knebworth to Parkston via Marley.

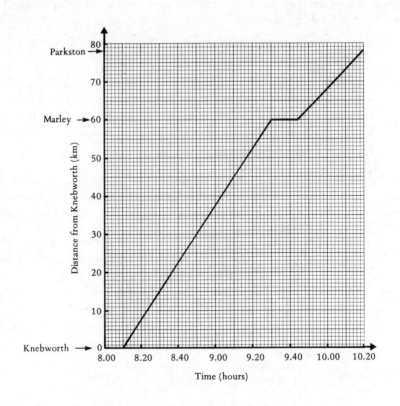

Use the graph to find

(a) the time at which the car
     (i)   leaves Knebworth,
     (ii) arrives in Marley,
     (iii) leaves Marley,
     (iv) arrives in Parkston,

(b) how long the car stops in Marley,

(c) how long the journey takes, including the stop,

(d) how far it is
     (i)   from Knebworth to Marley,
     (ii) from Knebworth to Parkston,

(e) the average speed for the whole journey.

$$\text{Remember that}\quad\text{Average speed} = \frac{\text{Total distance}}{\text{Total time}}$$

92

6   Jeff Chalmers leaves home one morning on a business trip. The graph represents his journey.

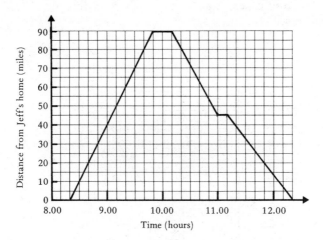

(a) How many stops does he make?

(b) How long is
   (i) his first stop,
   (ii) his second stop?

(c) How far is he from home at the furthest point?

(d) How long does it take him to get to the furthest point?

(e) What is his average speed for the first part of the journey?

(f) On the return journey, for how long does he drive
   (i) before he stops,
   (ii) after he stops?

(g) How far does he drive altogether?

(h) How long does the round trip take him?

(i) What is the average speed for the whole journey, including stops?

7   A manufacturer produces plastic jugs. The graph shows how the capacity of a jug, in millilitres, increases as the radius of its base, in centimetres, increases, e.g. a jug with a radius of 3 cm will hold 270 millilitres.

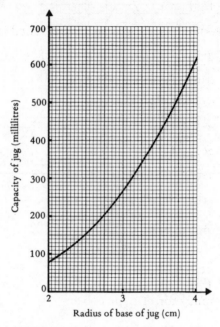

Radius of base of jug (cm)

(a) What is the capacity of a jug with radius
    (i) 2 cm, (ii) 4 cm, (iii) 3.5 cm?

(b) What is the radius of a jug that holds
    (i) 200 millilitres, (ii) 500 millilitres?

8   The graph shows the journeys of two trains between Highlane and Longbarrow.

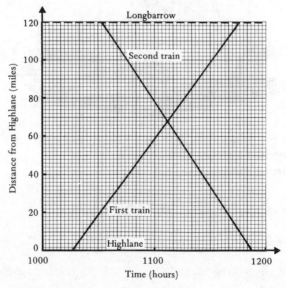

Time (hours)

94

(a) Look at the horizontal scale. What time does one large square represent? What time does one small square (i.e. 1 mm) represent?

Use the graph to find

(b) the time that the first train began and finished its journey,

(c) the time taken by the first train to complete its journey,

(d) the distance from Highlane to Longbarrow,

(e) the average speed of the first train,

(f) the time taken by the second train to complete its journey,

(g) the average speed of the second train,

(h) when, and where, the two trains pass,

(i) how far apart the two trains are at 1100.

9   This graph was obtained by measuring the heights of 50 fourth-form pupils. It shows the total number of pupils below a certain height, e.g. there are 9 pupils shorter than 140 cm.

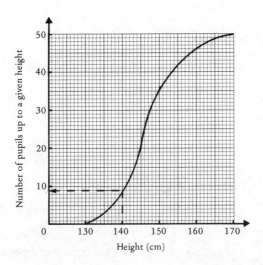

(a) How many pupils are shorter than
    (i) 145 cm, (ii) 150 cm, (iii) 162 cm?

(b) Use your answers to part (a) to find the number of pupils who are taller than
    (i) 145 cm, (ii) 150 cm, (iii) 162 cm.

(Assume that there is no pupil whose height is exactly 145 cm, 150 cm or 162 cm.)

10   The table shows how the area of a square increases as the length of a side increases.

Length of side (cm)	0	1	2	3	4	5
Area (cm²)	0	1	4	9	16	25

(a) Copy the diagram given below. Plot the points to represent this data, and draw a smooth curve to pass through these points.

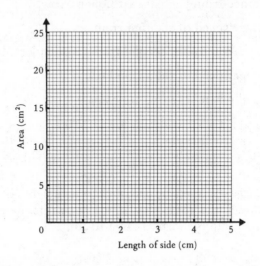

(b) Use your graph to find
   (i) the area of a square of side 3.6 cm,
   (ii) the length of a side of a square whose area is 20 cm².

Substitution in Formulae   26

1   Eddie calculates his wage by using the formula

$$\text{Wage} = \text{Number of hours} \times \text{Rate per hour}$$

(a) Use this formula to find Eddie's wage if
   (i) he works 36 hours at an hourly rate of £3,
   (ii) he works 40 hours at an hourly rate of £4.20,
   (iii) he works 37 hours at an hourly rate of £5.30.

(b) Use the same formula to find Eddie's hourly rate if he gets £174.80 for working 38 hours.

(c) How many hours does he work, if he earns £135 when the hourly rate is £3.75?

2 Use the formula

$$\text{Distance} = \text{Speed} \times \text{Time}$$

to find
(a) the distance travelled in 5 hours at 45 m.p.h.,
(b) the distance travelled in $4\frac{1}{2}$ hours at 50 km/hour.

3 Use the formula

$$\text{Volume of cuboid} = \text{Length} \times \text{Width} \times \text{Height}$$

to find the volume of a cuboid 12 cm long, 6 cm wide and 8 cm high.

4 Use the formula

$$\text{Time in Tokyo} = \text{Time in London} + 9 \text{ hours}$$

to find
(a) the time in Tokyo when it is 9 a.m. in London,
(b) the time in London when it is 4 p.m. in Tokyo.

5 Use the formula

$$\text{Charge for electricity} = \text{Cost per unit} \times \text{Number of units used}$$

to find
(a) the cost of 700 units at 6 p per unit,
(b) the cost per unit if 500 units cost £25.

6 Use the formula $S = \dfrac{PRT}{100}$ to find S, when $P = 500$, $R = 10$ and $T = 3$.

7 Use the formula $C = 2\pi r$ to find C when $\pi = 3.14$ and $r = 5$.

8 Use the formula $A = \frac{1}{2}bh$ to find A when $b = 15$ and $h = 8$.

9 Use the formula $C = \frac{5}{9}(F - 32)$ to find C when
(a) $F = 104$,   (b) $F = 212$,   (c) $F = 32$.

10 Use the formula $S = \dfrac{n(n + 1)}{2}$ to find S when

(a) $n = 10$,   (b) $n = 19$.

11 If $P = r^2 + 2s$, find
(a) the value of P when $r = 2$ and $s = 3$,
(b) the value of r^2 when $P = 16$ and $s = 4$,
(c) the value of s when $P = 25$ and $r = 3$.

12 Find the value of *abc* if
    (a) $a = 2$, $b = 3$, $c = 4$,   (b) $a = 2$, $b = 5$, $c = -5$,
    (c) $a = 3$, $b = 0$, $c = 1$.

13 Find the value of *ab + bc* if
    (a) $a = 3$, $b = 5$, $c = 1$,   (b) $a = 2$, $b = 0$, $c = 3$,
    (c) $a = 3$, $b = 2$, $c = -3$.

Symmetry and Transformations   27

1   Look at the letters in this word.

  (a) Which letters have
     (i) one axis of symmetry,
     (ii) rotational symmetry of order 2?
  (b) Which letter has
     (i) two axes of symmetry,
     (ii) both line symmetry and rotational symmetry?

2   Look at the letters in this word.

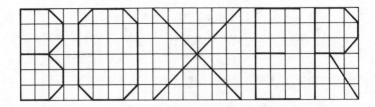

  (a) Which letter has rotational symmetry of order 2?
  (b) Which letter has rotational symmetry of order 4?
  (c) Which letter does not have an axis of symmetry?
  (d) Which letters have a vertical line as an axis of symmetry?
  (e) Which letters have a horizontal line as an axis of symmetry?

3 Copy each diagram and draw the axis of symmetry.

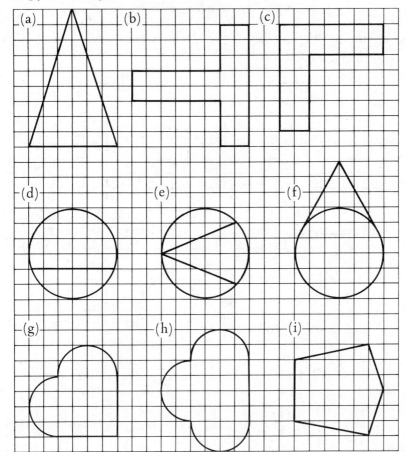

4 Copy each of the following diagrams, and draw the result of rotating each shape a quarter turn clockwise about A.

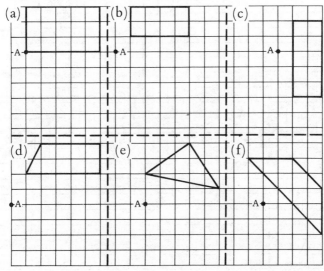

5 Copy each of the following diagrams, and draw the result of rotating each shape a quarter turn anticlockwise about A.

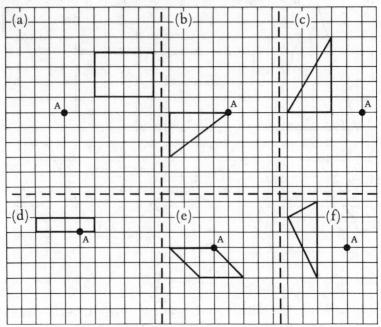

6 Copy each of the following diagrams, and draw the result of rotating each shape half a turn clockwise about A. Would the result be the same if you rotated anticlockwise instead of clockwise?

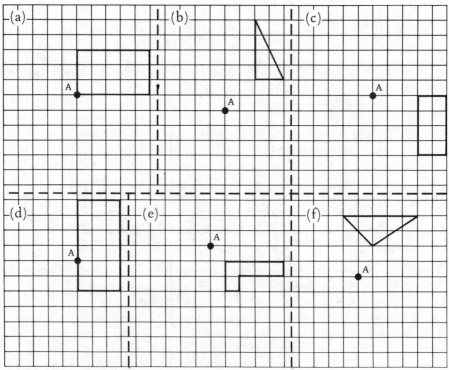

7 State the order of rotational symmetry about A for each of the following shapes.

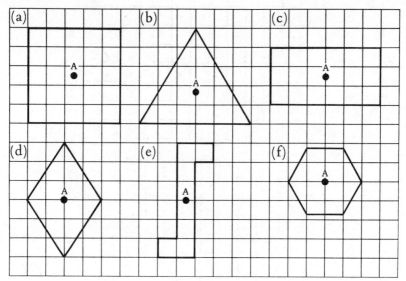

8 Copy each of the following diagrams, and draw the result of reflecting each shape in the given line.

(a)

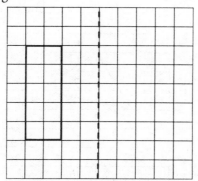

(b)

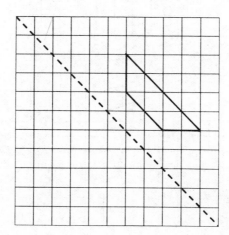

(c)

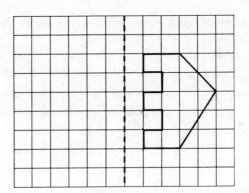

(d)

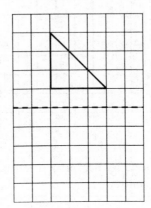

(e)

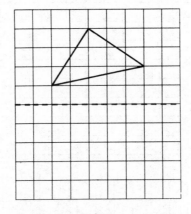

(f)

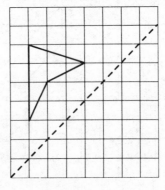

9 How many lines of symmetry are there for each of the given shapes?

(a)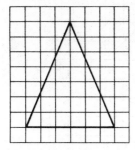

(b)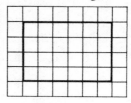

(c)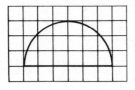

(d)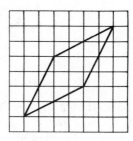

(e)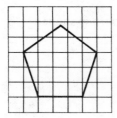

(f)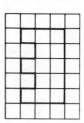

10

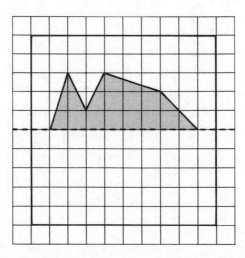

The tile shown in the diagram has one axis of symmetry. Copy the diagram on squared paper and complete the shading to show the full pattern.

11

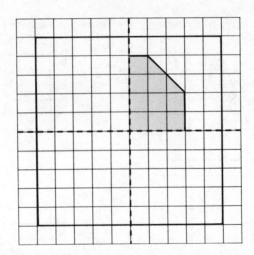

The tile shown in the diagram has two axes of symmetry.

(a) Copy the diagram on squared paper and complete the shading to show the full pattern.

(b) What fraction of the completed pattern is shaded?

12

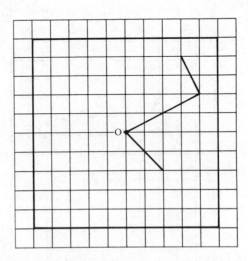

Copy the diagram on squared paper and complete the pattern so that there is rotational symmetry about O of order 2.

13

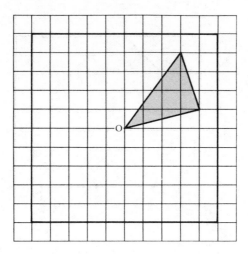

Copy the diagram on squared paper and complete the pattern so that there is rotational symmetry about O of order 4.

14

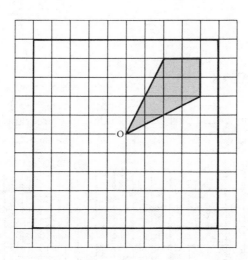

(a) Copy the diagram on squared paper and complete the pattern so that there is rotational symmetry about O of order 4.

(b) Does the completed pattern have line symmetry? If so, show any such lines on your diagram.

15

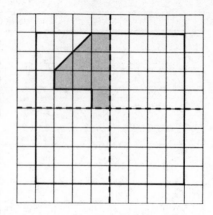

The tile shown in the diagram has two axes of symmetry.

(a) Copy the diagram on squared paper and complete the shading to show the full pattern.

(b) What fraction of the tile is shaded?

(c) What other type of symmetry does the full pattern have?

Tessellations

28

1 The diagram shows part of a tessellation of rectangles.

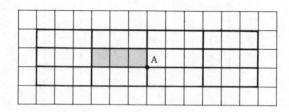

(a) How many rectangles come together at A?

(b) What do all the angles at A add up to?

(c) What size is the angle of the shaded rectangle at A?

(d) What size is each angle in a rectangle?

2 The diagram shows part of a tessellation of equilateral triangles.

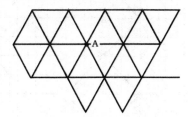

(a) What do all the angles at A add up to?
(b) How many equilateral triangles fit together at A?
(c) What is the size of each angle in an equilateral triangle?
(d) All the equilateral triangles that fit together at A form another shape. What name do we give to this shape? Is the shape regular? Draw part of a tessellation using this shape. What is the size of each angle in this shape?

3 The diagram shows two different shapes that tessellate.

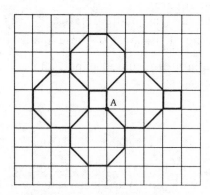

(a) Name the two shapes used.
(b) Is the smaller shape regular?
(c) Is the larger shape regular?
(d) What do the angles at point A add up to?
(e) What is the size of each angle in
   (i) the smaller shape,
   (ii) the larger shape?
(f) Copy the diagram, and add at least four more of each shape to it.

4

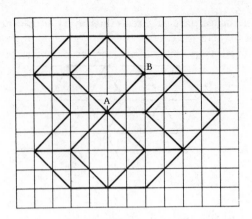

The diagram shows a tessellation of a tile, using two shapes — a square and another quadrilateral.

(a) What do the angles around a point add to?

(b) What special name do we give to the smaller quadrilateral?

(c) Use the point A to find the size of each acute angle in the smaller quadrilateral.

(d) Use the point B to find the size of each obtuse angle in the smaller quadrilateral.

(e) By counting squares, find the area of
   (i) one of the squares,
   (ii) one of the smaller quadrilaterals.

   What is the ratio of the areas of these quadrilaterals?

(f) Copy the diagram on squared paper, and add at least four more of each shape.

5 Use squared paper to show that tiles of the given shape can be used to cover a floor, with no spaces between them. Give at least eight tiles to show how a regular pattern can be built up.

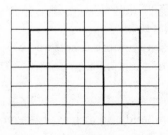

6 A tessellation is to be constructed on the grid using tiles in the shape of a cross. One tile is drawn for you. Use dotted paper, and show, by drawing at least five more tiles, how the regular pattern can be built up.

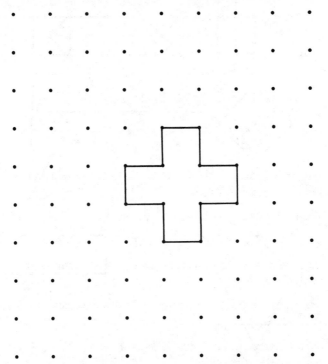

7 The diagram shows five triangular tiles placed in a regular pattern, with no spaces between them. The tiles are said to tessellate.

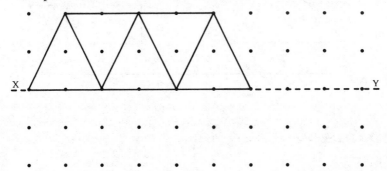

(a) Copy the pattern, and continue the line with another three tiles on the right-hand side.

(b) Continue the pattern with a second row of tiles, placed so that the resulting pattern of two rows of tiles is symmetrical about the line XY.

(c) Look at one tile. Is the triangle isosceles, equilateral or neither of these?

8 Use dotted paper to show how each of the following shapes tessellate.
   Draw at least six of each to show a regular pattern.

(a)

(b)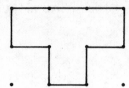

(c)

(d)

(e)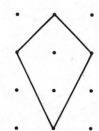

(f)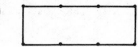

(g)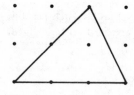

(h)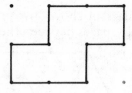

Probability   29

1 There are 16 girls in a class of 24. A pupil is chosen at random. What
   is the probability that the chosen pupil
   (a) is a girl,   (b) is a boy?

2 A box contains 12 chocolates with soft centres and 18 chocolates
   with hard centres. How many chocolates are there in the box? Ellen
   chooses a chocolate at random from the box. What is the probability
   that it has a hard centre?

3   Peter has a bag containing 30 pieces of Lego. Eight are coloured red, ten are coloured yellow and the rest are black. Jim draws out one piece of Lego. What is the probability that the colour of this piece is

(a) red,   (b) black,   (c) white?

4   Three of the six apples in a bag are bad. Ray takes one apple. What is the probability that it is a good one?

5   Rita chooses a month at random from the 12 months of the year. What is the probability that the chosen month

(a) begins with the letter J,

(b) begins with a vowel?

6   A day is chosen at random from the month of June. What is the probability that the date of this day

(a) is even,

(b) will divide exactly by ten,

(c) will divide exactly by five?

7   One letter is chosen at random from the letters in the word 'SCHOOL'. What is the probability that it is O?

8   Paul writes the whole numbers from one to ten. He asks Kathryn to choose one of these numbers. What is the probability that Kathryn chooses a prime number?

9   The pupils of form 5P are raffling an iced cake to raise money for Christmas decorations. They sell 250 tickets at 5p each. Ying bought five tickets. What is the probability that he wins the cake?

10   In a class, there are 12 girls and 16 boys. One person is chosen at random. What is the probability that the person chosen is

(a) a girl,   (b) a boy?

11   A whole number is chosen from the first 12 whole numbers. What is the probability that the chosen number is

(a) less than ten,

(b) a two-digit number,

(c) exactly divisible by three,

(d) an even number?

12   One letter is chosen at random from the letters in the word 'TELEVISION'. What is the probability that it is

(a) a vowel,   (b) a consonant,   (c) E?

1 The pictogram shows the population of Edom in 1961, 1971 and 1981.

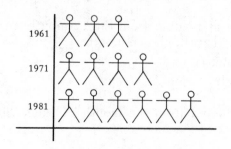

represents 200 people.

(a) How many people lived in Edom
(i) in 1961, (ii) in 1981?

(b) How many more people lived there in 1981 than in 1971?

(c) In 1991, it is expected that the population will be 600 more than in 1981. How many 웃 symbols are needed to show the total population in 1991?

2 Twenty-four pupils were asked how many upstairs rooms they had at home. The results are shown in the pie chart.

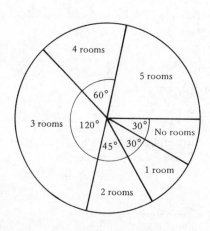

(a) Find the missing angle on the pie chart.

(b) Copy and complete the following table.

	Number of upstairs rooms					
	0	1	2	3	4	5
Number of pupils						

(c) How many pupils lived in homes
    (i) with three or more upstairs rooms,
    (ii) with less than three upstairs rooms?

(d) How many upstairs rooms are there altogether?

3 Twelve women are asked how many children they each have in their family. The results are shown in the pie chart.

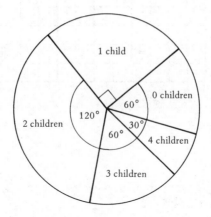

(a) Copy and complete the following table.

	Number of children				
	0	1	2	3	4
Number of women					

(b) How many children are there altogether?

(c) What fraction of those asked had one child?

(d) One of the 12 women is chosen at random. What is the probability that she has two children?

4 500 people were asked to complete a questionnaire and to return it within seven days. The bar chart shows the number of questionnaires returned daily.

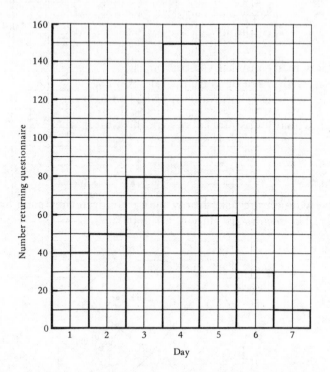

(a) How many questionnaires were returned
   (i) on the third day,
   (ii) on the last day?

(b) How many more questionnaires were returned on the fourth day than on the second day?

(c) How many questionnaires were returned altogether?

(d) On which day were the most questionnaires returned?

(e) How many people did not return a questionnaire?

(f) What fraction of the people returned their questionnaires?

5   The bar chart shows the number of cars using the ferry to a Scottish island one week last August.

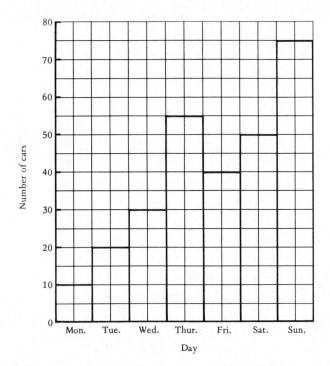

(a) How many cars did the ferry carry
     (i) on Wednesday,
     (ii) on Saturday?

(b) On which day of the week did the ferry carry most cars?

(c) On which day of the week did the ferry carry the least number of cars?

(d) What was the total number of cars carried in the week?

(e) What was the average number of cars carried per day during the week?

(f) In the following week, the average number of cars carried per day went down by five. How many cars did the ferry carry that week?

(g) Would you expect the average number of cars carried per day to be the same in February as in August? Give a reason for your answer.

6   A group of pupils recorded the number of pets owned by their family. The results are shown in this bar chart.

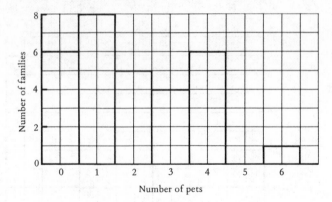

Number of families (vertical axis)
Number of pets (horizontal axis)

(a) How many families own
   (i) one pet,
   (ii) four pets?
(b) How many families are there altogether?
(c) How many families own
   (i) more than three pets,
   (ii) fewer than three pets?
(d) What is the most popular number of pets?
(e) What fraction of the families have one pet?
(f) What percentage of the families have more than three pets?

7   The pupils in form 5S were given a geography test which was marked out of 10. The marks are given below

    6   9   5   7   7 10   4   8   9   5
    8 10   2   9   5   8   7   8   8   7
    4   8   6   8   3   5   8   7   2   6

(a) Copy and complete this table.

Mark	Tally	Number of pupils
1		
2		
3		
4		
5		
6		
7		
8		
9		
10		

(b) How many pupils took the test?

(c) How many pupils scored
   (i) more than 7,   (ii) less than 5?

(d) Copy and complete the bar chart given below.

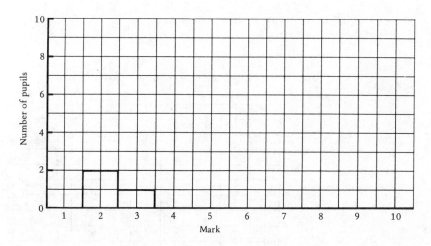

(e) What fraction of the class scored
   (i) less than 5,   (ii) more than 7?

(f) What percentage of the class scored
   (i) less than 6,   (ii) 7 or more?

(g) A pupil is chosen at random from this class. What is the probability that this pupil scored
   (i) 6,   (ii) more than 8?

117

8 In a random survey in Blackwood the ages of 40 people were

62 32 87 62 48 9 42 53 41 24
29 47 38 21 54 72 52 3 73 37
48 49 78 67 33 64 39 12 45 69
68 79 45 65 59 15 84 38 55 18

(a) Copy and complete this table.

Age	Tally	Frequency
1–10		
11–20		
21–30		
31–40		
41–50		
51–60		
61–70		
71–80		
81–90		
	Total	

(b) How many people were aged
  (i) 21 to 30,
  (ii) under 21?

(c) Copy and complete the bar chart given below.

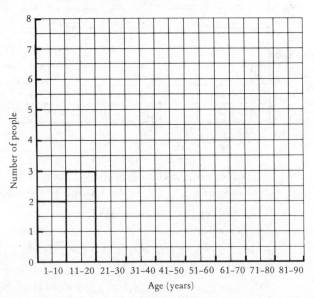

118

(d) What fraction of those surveyed were
   (i) under 21,
   (ii) over 60?

The population of Blackwood is 2880. If this survey is typical

(e) how many of the population are
   (i) under 21,
   (ii) over 60?

(f) What percentage of the population are
   (i) aged 41 to 50,
   (ii) over 30?

(g) A person is chosen at random from the group surveyed. What is the probability that the person is aged between 41 and 70?

9   At the school Christmas Fair, form 5Q organised a competition to guess the number of sweets in a jar, correct to the nearest 10.

(a) The first to try were a family of five. Their guesses were: father 120, mother 200, Tony 140, Sandra 150, Ceri 140. What was the mean guess for this family?

(b) During the next half an hour the guesses were:

    130 150 140 210 140 200 160 130 150 200
    190 200 160 170 150 150 140 130 160 140
    150 170 160 190 150 180 140 150 180 170
    180 120 120 120 190 160 200 190 170 110

   Not including the family in part (a).
   (i) What was the highest guess?
   (ii) What was the lowest guess?
   (iii) How many guesses were there altogether?
   (iv) Copy and complete the table overleaf – the first three columns of guesses have been done for you.

119

Guess	Tally	Frequency
110		
120	I I	
130	I	
140	I	
150	I I	
160	I I	
170	I	
180	I	
190	I	
200	I	
210		

(c) Copy and complete the bar chart.

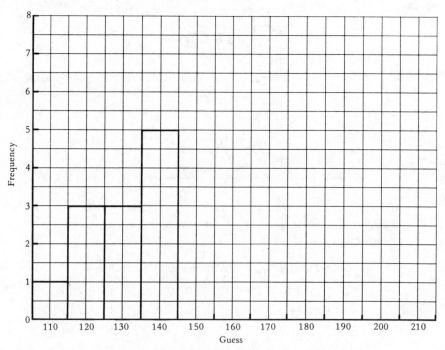

(d) What is the most common guess?

(e) The total for these guesses is 6400. What is the mean guess?

(f) How many people thought there were fewer than 150 sweets in the jar?

Part 2: Revision Papers 1–20

Revision Paper **1**

1   Write
    (a) 3127 in words,
    (b) one thousand and forty-seven in figures.

2   Round the number 7294
    (a) to the nearest 100,
    (b) to the nearest 1000.

3   3, 8, 12, 5, 7, 9
    (a) Which of these numbers
         (i) are prime numbers,
         (ii) are multiples of 3,
         (iii) are odd numbers?
    (b) Write the numbers in order, smallest first.
    (c) Write all the factors of the largest number.

4   Work out the value of abc when $a = 5$, $b = 7$ and $c = 3$.

5   (a) Give 10p as a fraction of 50p.
    (b) Give 75p as a fraction of £1.
    (c) What fraction is £8 of £10?

6

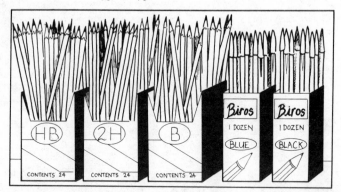

(a) Helen buys four biros at 24p each. How much will this cost her?
     How much change will she get from £1?

(b) Norman paid 64p for eight pencils. How much does one pencil
     cost? What must he pay for five pencils?

7   The five waitresses in a café share tips equally. One day the tips they
    received were £2.60, £4.30, £3.70, £2.90 and £2.85. How much did
    each get?

8   Four coins in Ted's pocket have a total value of 73p. What could the
    coins be?

Revision Paper 2

1. Write in words
   (a) the number 1988, (b) the year 1988.

2. There were eighty-two thousand nine hundred and seven spectators at Wembley last Saturday.
   (a) Write this number in figures.
   (b) Write this number correct to the nearest thousand.

3.  What fraction of this shape is
   (a) shaded,
   (b) unshaded?

4. Complete the following statements.
   (a) $\dfrac{3}{4} = \dfrac{}{12} = \dfrac{}{16} = \dfrac{18}{}$ (b) $\dfrac{1}{4} + \dfrac{3}{8} = \dfrac{}{8} + \dfrac{3}{8} =$

5. On a certain day, the temperature at midday was 12°C. By midnight, the temperature had fallen by 19°C. What was the temperature at midnight?

6. Neil divides £8 by 3 using his calculator. The display shows 2.6666666. What is the answer correct to the nearest penny? He gives this amount to Sue and the same to Vernon. How much does he have left for himself?

7.

   New cars lose about 20% of their value in the first year. About how much will this car be worth when it is one year old?

8. In a small business four workers earn £105 per week each, while the other three earn £126 per week each.
   (a) What is the total weekly wage bill?
   (b) What is the average weekly wage of these seven workers?

Revision Paper 3

1   What do you have to subtract from 22 to get 15?

2   Find the remainder when 45 is divided by 6.

3   (a) Write the place value of the figure 7 in the number 54.27.
    (b) Find the difference in the actual value of the two 4s in the number 4347.

4   Find
    (a) $\frac{1}{4}$ of 84 p,   (b) $\frac{2}{5}$ of £20.

5   Find
    (a) $\frac{7}{12} + \frac{1}{6}$ (b) $\frac{3}{4} - \frac{7}{12}$

6   Sally thinks of a number, doubles it and adds eight. The answer is 26. What number did Sally think of?

7   Work out the value of $2l + 2b$ when $l = 8$ and $b = 3$.

8

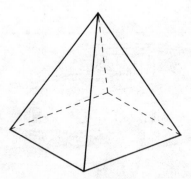

Naomi brought a square-based pyramid home as a souvenir from a holiday in Egypt.
(a) How many faces does it have?
(b) How many edges does it have?

9   Adrian is going to cook the evening meal for his parents. His mother is due home at 5.30 and his father at 5.45. He estimates that it will take him 70 minutes to prepare. At what time should he start to prepare?

10 The diagram shows part of the design for a square tile that has rotational symmetry of side 4.

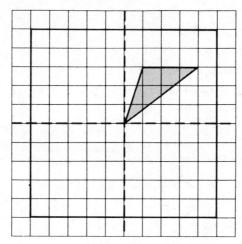

(a) Copy and complete the design.
(b) What fraction of the complete tile is shaded?
(c) Does the tile have an axis of symmetry?

Revision Paper   4

1 Put the numbers 18, 11, 88, 81 and 8 in order of size, smallest first.

2 Place the correct symbol >, < or = between each of the following pairs of numbers.
   (a) 7   17   (b) −5   3
   (c) $\frac{4}{5}$ 0.8   (d) 0.73   0.37

3 In a class of 28 pupils, 18 are boys. What fraction of the class
   (a) are boys,   (b) are girls?

4   1
                              1   2   1
                           1   3   3   1
                        1   4   6   4   1
                     1   a   10   b   5   1
                  1   6   15   c   15   6   1

   Study the pattern. What is the value of each of the letters a, b and c?

5 What is the next number in the sequence 1, 5, 9, 13, ... ?

6 The ages of three brothers are 14 years 7 months, 15 years 10 months and 17 years 7 months.
   (a) What is the total age of the three brothers in years and months?
   (b) What is their average age?
   (c) How much will their average age rise in exactly one year's time?

7 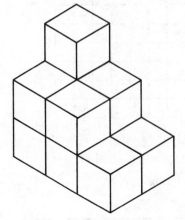 The diagram shows a stack of cubes. How many cubes are there?

8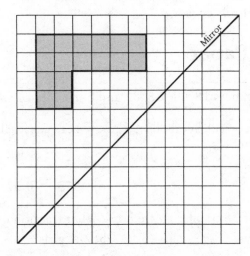

The diagram shows a shape and a mirror line. Copy the diagram on to squared paper and draw the reflection of the shape.

9 Pat and John Willis have two children. Given that the probability of having a boy is the same as the probability of having a girl, find the probability that
   (a) both children are girls,
   (b) they have one boy and one girl.

10 A group of seven children, three boys and four girls win £490 in a competition. Each child is given an equal share of the money. Find

(a) the amount each child receives,

(b) the total amount received by the boys,

(c) the total amount received by the girls.

Revision Paper   5

1   What must be added to 56 to get 123?

2   Write all the whole numbers from 1 to 10 that are
    (a) prime numbers,
    (b) multiples of 5,
    (c) odd but not prime,
    (d) factors of 12.

3

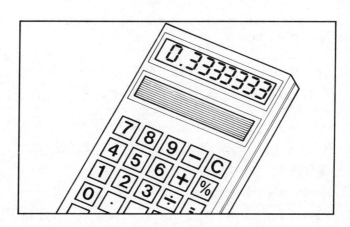

A calculator was used to divide two numbers. The answer shown on the display was

0.3333333

(a) What could the two numbers be?

(b) Can you give two other numbers that give the same answer?

4

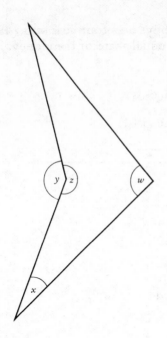

The diagram shows an arrowhead.

(a) Use your protractor to measure the size of
    (i) w,
    (ii) x,
    (iii) y.

(b) Calculate z.

5 Work out the value of $2l + 2b$ when $l = 10$ and $b = 9$.

6 What is the remainder
(a) when 4217 is divided by 4,

(b) when 1435 is divided by 9?

7 The times in minutes taken by a group of pupils to complete a test are given in the table.

Time (in minutes)	45	46	47	48	49	50	51
Number of pupils	2	4	5	8	7	3	1

(a) How many pupils are there in the group?

(b) Draw a bar chart to represent this information. Use 1 cm for each pupil on the vertical axis.

(c) Which time occurs most often?

(d) What fraction of the group complete the test in less than 47 minutes?

(e) What percentage of the group finish the test in less than 47 minutes?

8 Construct a triangle ABC in which AB = 12 cm, AC = 9 cm and BC = 10 cm.

9   Penny has six 10p coins and eight 5p coins, while Paul has sixteen 2p coins and one 50p coin. Who has the more money, and by how much, Penny or Paul?

10 The circumference of a trundle wheel is 1 m. How many times does the wheel turn in going $\frac{1}{2}$ km?

Revision Paper   6

1   Round 5555
    (a) to the nearest 10,
    (b) to the nearest 100,
    (c) to the nearest 1000.

2   Write each of these numbers as the sum of two prime numbers.
    (a) 8   (b) 9   (c) 12

3   Terry bought a pack of 36 screws. He used 24 of them. What fraction of the pack
    (a) were used,   (b) were unused?

4   The area of a square is 64 cm².
    (a) What is the length of one side?
    (b) Find the perimeter of the square.

5   Write all the two-figure numbers you can make from the figures 3, 4 and 5. No figure can be repeated. For example, 55 is not allowed.

6   Edwin thinks of a number, doubles it, and takes away 7. The answer is 13. What number did Edwin think of?

7   Imran is going to cycle the 268 miles from Leeds to Exeter. After the first three days, he has cycled 123 miles.
    (a) What was his average number of miles per day for the first three days?
    (b) How many miles remain to be cycled?
    (c) If Imran continues to cycle at the same average speed, how many more days will he require to complete the journey? (Part of a day counts as a whole day.)

8   Look at this word.

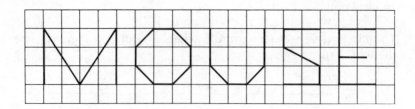

(a) How many axes of symmetry does the second letter have?

(b) Which letters have rotational symmetry? Give the order of symmetry in each case.

(c) Is there any letter that does not have line symmetry?

(d) Which letters have a vertical axis of symmetry?

(e) Which letters have a horizontal axis of symmetry?

9   The dates of birth of three children are:

Julie   14–3–73
Dennis   14–1–72
Johanne   14–8–73

(a) Who is the eldest and by how many months?

(b) Who is the youngest and by how many months?

(c) In which year will the youngest be 40?

(d) In which year will the eldest be 50?

10 The distribution in the table gives the marks obtained by 100 students in a geography examination.

Marks	10–19	20–29	30–39	40–49	50–59	60–69	70–79
Number of students	8	13	16	24	20	10	9

(a) On graph paper, draw a bar chart to represent this distribution.

(b) Write down the modal class.

Revision Paper 7

1 (a) Write two numbers that add up to 5.2.

(b) Write two numbers that, when multiplied, give 3.6.

(c) The difference between two numbers is 1.8. What could the numbers be?

2 Look at the number 347.86. Write the place value of

(a) the figure 4,   (b) the figure 8,   (c) the figure 6.

3 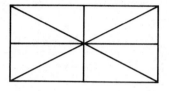 Sketch this diagram. Shade $\frac{5}{8}$ of it.

4 When two numbers are added, their sum is 7. When they are multiplied together, the answer is 12. What are the numbers?

5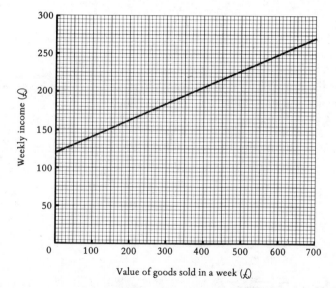

Value of goods sold in a week (£)

The graph shows the weekly income of Tom Halley. It is made up of two parts – basic weekly wage, plus commission based on the value of goods sold in the week. Use the graph to estimate

(a) the basic weekly wage,

(b) Tom's income when he sells goods to the value of £400,

(c) the value of the goods sold when Tom earns £270,

(d) the commission Tom gets when he sells goods to the value of £450.

131

6   What is the remainder
    (a) when 6321 is divided by 8,
    (b) when 927 is divided by 5?

7   How many hundredths must be added to 5.71 to make a total of 6?

8   Write the 24-hour clock time which is 55 minutes before
    (a) 1827,   (b) 0032.

9   A jug holds $1\frac{1}{2}$ litres. How many glasses, each with a capacity of 125 millilitres, can be filled from this jug?

10

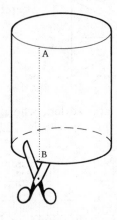

The diagram shows a mathematical shape that has been made from a thin piece of card. There is no top or bottom.

(a) What is its name?

(b) A cut is made along the line AB, and the card is opened out flat. What is the shape of the card?

Revision Paper   8

1   What must be multiplied by 6 to get 42?

2   Write 36 747
    (a) correct to the nearest 100,   (b) correct to the nearest 1000.

3   Find the difference between the value of the two fives in the number 355.2.

4   In a survey, 250 people were asked which television channel they liked best. 100 chose ITV and 50 said that they did not have a television set.

(a) What fraction of the people asked chose ITV?

(b) What percentage of the people asked did not have a television set?

(c) How many people had a television set, but did not prefer ITV?

5   The postage on a small parcel to be sent by first-class post is 51p. How can Jean pay the correct postage using only 18p stamps and 5p stamps?

6   A walker covers 13 km in 2 hours. What is her average speed in kilometres per hour?

7

When Mr and Mrs Miles and their two children were on holiday in Majorca, they went on a coach trip. The prices are shown above.

(a) Find the total cost of the trip in pesetas.

(b) What was the cost in pounds, if the exchange rate was £1 ≡ 200 pesetas?

Which building society pays the highest rate of interest?

9

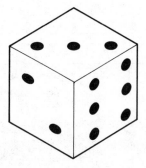

The diagram shows an ordinary dice.

(a) What is the total of all the dots on the dice?

(b) The sum of the dots on opposite faces is always the same. What must this sum be?

(c) How many dots are there on the face opposite to the 2?

(d) The diagram shows a net for this cube. Copy and complete the diagram to show the numbers of dots on each face.

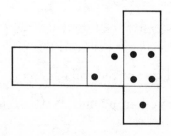

10   The bar chart shows the number of bedrooms in the properties in a street.

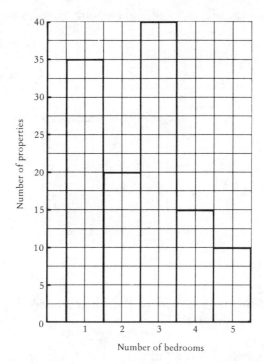

Number of bedrooms

(a) How many four-bedroomed properties are there?

(b) How many single-bedroomed properties are there?

(c) How many more three-bedroomed properties than five-bedroomed properties are there?

(d) How many properties are there in the street?

(e) How many bedrooms are there in total in all the three-bedroomed properties?

(f) How many bedrooms are there in the street?

(g) On average, each bedroom is used by two people. How many people live in the street?

(h) John stops at a property at random. Which of the following is most likely?
      A it has fewer than three bedrooms,
      B it has exactly three bedrooms,
      C it has more than three bedrooms.

(i) What fraction of the properties have more than three bedrooms?

Revision Paper   9

1   Jean packs eggs in trays of 20. How many trays are required for 560 eggs?

2   7, 8, 9, 10, 11, 12, 13

   How many of these numbers are
   (a) odd,
   (b) even,
   (c) prime,
   (d) multiples of 3,
   (e) factors of 14?

3

4		
8	7	
9		

   Complete the magic square so that the numbers in every row, column and diagonal add up to 21.

4   Jerry's calculator has a fault. The $+$ button is marked $-$ and the $-$ button is marked $+$.

   He wants to work out $(7 - 4) \times (7 + 4)$.
   (a) What is the right answer?
   (b) What answer does Jerry's calculator give?
   (c) Can you explain what has happened?

5   The exchange rate for Italian lire is 1340 lire to the £1 sterling. Calculate
   (a) the number of lire that would be exchanged for £120,
   (b) the amount of pounds sterling that would be received for 6968 lire.

6   Find the average (mean) of 81, 82, 84, 86, 87.

7   The time needed to roast a joint is 20 minutes to the pound and 20 minutes over.
   (a) How many minutes will it take to roast a 5 lb joint of beef? How many hours is this?
   (b) A joint of beef takes 1 hour 20 minutes to roast. How heavy is it?
   (c) Another joint takes $2\frac{1}{2}$ hours. How heavy is this joint?

8

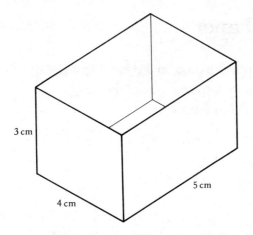

3 cm

4 cm

5 cm

The diagram shows an open rectangular box. The box is cut down all four vertical edges and the four sides folded over flat.

(a) What is the perimeter of the base of the box?

(b) What is the area of the base?

(c) Draw a sketch of the card when it has been folded out flat.

(d) Find
   (i) the perimeter, (ii) the area, of the flat shape.

9 The following figures represent the readings on an electricity meter at the beginning and end of the same quarter.

First reading	Second reading
17656	18787

Find

(a) the total number of units of electricity used during the quarter,

(b) the average weekly consumption of electricity (1 quarter ≡ 13 weeks),

(c) the total cost of the electricity used during the quarter, when the following charges apply.

$$\begin{array}{ll} \text{Standing charge} & £8.50 \\ \text{Cost of each unit} & 5.8\,\text{p} \end{array}$$

10 A wheel is rotating at the rate of 20 revolutions per minute.

(a) How many revolutions does it make in
   (i) 40 minutes, (ii) 1 hour?

(b) How long does it take to make 1000 revolutions?

1   Hazel has five 10p coins and three 20p coins.

   (a)   How many 18p stamps can she buy?

   (b)   How much is left over?

2   Find

   (a)   the square of 4,

   (b)   the square root of 25,

   (c)   the cube of 3.

3   A calculator was used to divide two numbers.

   (a)   The answer that appeared on the display was 0.25. What could the numbers be?

   (b)   On another occasion the answer was 0.666 666 6. What could the numbers be?

4   Work out the value of $\frac{1}{2}bh$ when $b = 14$ and $h = 5$.

5

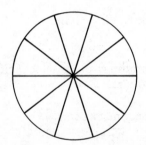

Sketch this diagram. Shade $\frac{3}{5}$ of it.

6   Jill and Norma share a job as a petrol attendant. Jill works 4 days and Norma does the remaining 3 days each week. Jill earns £56 each week. Assume they are paid at the same rate.

   (a)   How much does Norma earn?

   (b)   How much would Jill earn if she worked a full week?

7   The radius of a circular table is 46 cm. Find

   (a)   its diameter,

   (b)   its circumference ($\pi = 3.14$).

8   Harry bought some books from Mail Order Books PLC.

   (a)   Copy and complete his invoice shown opposite.

   (b)   What is the price of *Cooking for One*?

   (c)   How much does one copy of the *Pop and Rock Annual* cost?

   (d)   *Stonehenge* was out of stock. How much refund should Harry get? Don't forget to allow for the discount.

Mail Order Books PLC							
Book number				Title	Qty.	£	p
C	8	7	2	*The Snow King*	1	5	75
C	4	9	3	*Pop and Rock Annual*	2	9	90
C	8	2	1	*Cooking for One*	1		
A		4	7	*Stonehenge*	1	12	50
				Order value		35	–
				Less 20% discount			
				Sub-total			
				Add post and packing		1	95
				Total cost			

9   The bar chart shows the average daily maximum temperature in London and on the Greek island of Poros, during the summer months. It also shows the average daily number of hours of sunshine in Poros.

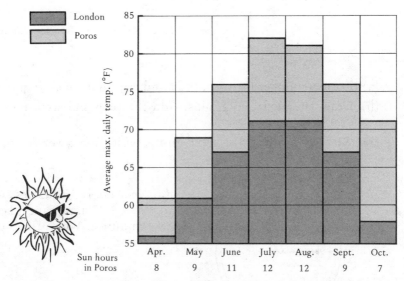

(a) Estimate the average maximum daily temperature in Poros
   (i) in June,   (ii) in July.

(b) Estimate the average maximum daily temperature in London
   (i) in June,   (ii) in July.

(c) What is the average number of hours of sunshine in Poros during the month of June?

(d) What is the total number of hours of sunshine in Poros during the month of June?

(e) Estimate how much higher the average daily temperature in Poros is in October than the average daily temperature in London.

10   To convert kilometres into miles the rule is

Divide by 8, then multiply by 5.

Use this rule to convert

(a) 80 km into miles,

(b) 112 km into miles,

(c) 144 km per hour into miles per hour.

Revision Paper **11**

1   Use the equation $P = a + b + c$ to find
   (a) the value of P if $a = 5$, $b = 9$ and $c = 7$,
   (b) the value of c if $P = 20$, $a = 6$ and $b = 7$.

2

(a) Form a number list from the number of dots in each group.

(b) Draw the next two groups. Add the fifth and sixth numbers to your list.

(c) Without drawing the next group, write the seventh number in the list.

3

(a) In school, the first lesson starts at 9.05 a.m. and lasts 35 minutes. What time does it end?

(b) The eighth lesson ends at 3.35 p.m. and lasts 40 minutes. What time does it start?

4 Tania thinks of a number, trebles it, and adds 12. The answer is 36. What number did Tania think of?

5 At the beginning of the year, Caroline has £40 in the building society. She saves the same amount each month, and at the end of 3 months has £(40 + 3x) in the account.

(a) In terms of x, how much does she save each month?

(b) How much does she have after 6 months?

(c) How many months must pass before she has £90 in the account, if she saves £10 each month?

6 (a) Write the date which is
      (i) 7 months later than 5 November,
      (ii) 6 months before 22 April.

(b) A letter posted in America on 27 August was delivered in Manchester on 3 September. How many days was it in the post? Include either the day of posting or the day of delivery, but not both.

7
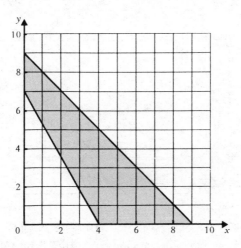

Use the formula

$$\text{Area of a triangle} = \tfrac{1}{2} \text{ Base} \times \text{Height}$$

to find the area of the shaded quadrilateral.

8   Tomzin's mortgage repayments are £8.30 per month per £1000 borrowed. He has a mortgage for £20 000 which is repayable over 25 years.

(a) How many thousand pounds does he borrow?

(b) How much do his repayments come to for one month?

(c) How many months are there in 25 years?

(d) How much do his repayments come to altogether?

9   This railway map has a scale of 1 cm to 10 km.

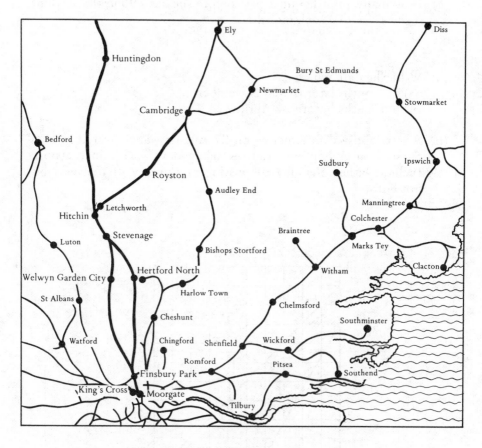

(a) How far is it 'as the crow flies' from Stevenage to Audley End?

(b) How far is it from Stevenage to Audley End by train via Hitchin and Cambridge?

(c) How far is it by train from King's Cross to Huntingdon?

(d) How far is it, in a straight line, from Moorgate to Cambridge?

(In parts (b) and (c), use a piece of string or a pair of dividers set at 1 cm.)

10 Look at this diagram.

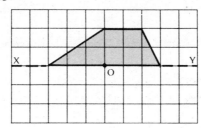

Copy the diagram on squared paper.

(a) What name do we give to the shaded figure?

(b) Draw the quadrilateral obtained by rotating the given quadrilateral through half a turn about O.

(c) Does the completed figure have any line of symmetry?

Revision Paper 12

1 What must be divided by 5 to get 8?

2 Find

(a) $\frac{3}{5} + \frac{1}{5}$ (b) $\frac{4}{5} - \frac{2}{5}$

3 The difference between two positive numbers is 3. When the numbers are multiplied together the answer is 28. What are the numbers?

4 An aeroplane from the West Indies is due to land at 1406. Because of a strong tail wind, it arrives 45 minutes early. What time does it arrive?

5

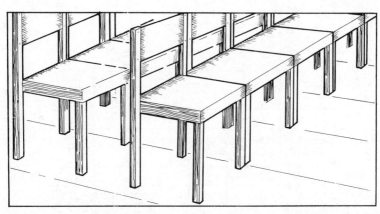

Each row in a school hall has 20 seats. There are 420 seats. How many rows are there?

6 Six coins in Sandra's purse have a total value of 93p. What could the coins be?

7 Nita's calculator has a fault. The $\boxed{+}$ button is marked $\boxed{-}$ and the $\boxed{-}$ button is marked $\boxed{+}$.
She wants to work out $(7 - 4) \times (5 + 3)$.
(a) What is the right answer?
(b) What answer does Nita's calculator give?

8

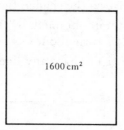

A square has an area of 1600 cm².
(a) What is the length of each side of the square?
(b) What is the perimeter of the square?

9 A wheel makes one revolution every 20 seconds.
(a) How many revolutions does it make in
(i) 10 minutes,
(ii) 2 hours?
(b) How long does it take to make
(i) 100 revolutions,
(ii) 6000 revolutions?

10 The diagram shows a shape and a mirror line. Copy the diagram on squared paper and draw the reflection of the shape.

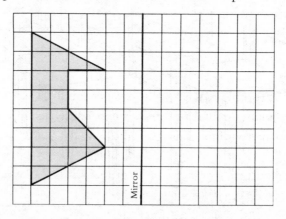

Revision Paper   **13**

1   (a) Write 0.3 as a fraction.

    (b) Give $\frac{7}{8}$ as a decimal.

2   (a) Which is the larger, 1.07 or 1.16?

    (b) Which is the smaller, 0.61 or 0.099?

3   Geoff, Hilary and Iris pay £12.46 between them for a meal. Geoff pays £3.96 and Hilary pays £4.54. How much does Iris pay?

4   Use the formula $A = \dfrac{12}{a}$ to find

    (a) A when $a = 4$,

    (b) a when $A = 6$.

5

London

Day Excursion £12.50
Children – half-fare

What is the rail fare for two adults and three children?

6   A wheel is turning at 20 revolutions per minute.

    (a) How many revolutions does it make each hour?

    (b) How many minutes does it take to make 5000 revolutions?

7   The total cost of x oranges and y grapefruit is $(12x + 25y)$ p.

    (a) What is the cost of an orange?

    (b) What is the cost of a grapefruit?

    (c) Find the total cost of 4 oranges and 3 grapefruit.

8 The table shows the distances between several places in England.

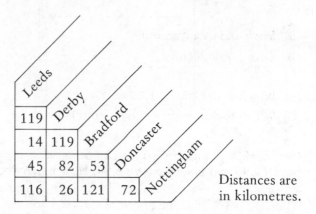

Distances are in kilometres.

(a) What is the distance
   (i) from Bradford to Derby,
   (ii) from Leeds to Nottingham?

(b) The circuit for a motor rally goes from Doncaster to Nottingham, on to Derby and then straight back to Doncaster. What is the total length of the circuit?

(c) A car took 20 minutes for the second stage of the journey (from Nottingham to Derby). What was its average speed for this stage?

(d) The whole journey took 2 hours. What was the average speed for the rally?

9

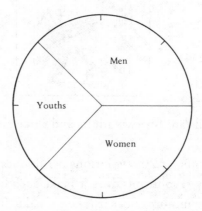

360 men, women and youths work at a factory. Use the pie chart to find

(a) the number of women,   (b) the number of youths,

working at the factory.

10

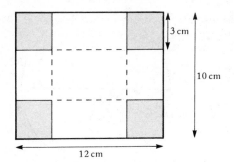

Four equal squares (which are shaded) of side 3 cm are cut from the corners of a rectangular piece of card measuring 12 cm by 10 cm. The card is then folded about the dotted lines to make a box.

(a) Find the length and breadth of the base of the box.

(b) How deep is the box?

(c) What is the volume of the box?

(d) How much card is wasted?

(e) What fraction of the original card is wasted?

Revision Paper   **14**

1 Write these numbers in order of size, smallest first.

$$0.525, \ 0.55, \ 0.556, \ 0.077$$

2 Twenty-eight marbles are divided between Len and Mel in the ratio 3:4, respectively. How many does Mel get?

3 In a school of 1350 pupils, 1242 pupils are present.

(a) How many pupils are absent?

(b) What percentage of the pupils are absent?

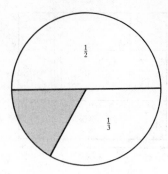

4

What fraction of this circle is

(a) unshaded,   (b) shaded?

5 Use each of the figures 1, 5, 8 and 9 once only to write the largest possible four-figure number.

6 Oranges cost 12 p each. Mavis has three 50 p coins and five 20 p coins.

(a) How many oranges can she buy?

(b) How much money is left over?

7 Vernon is paid at a basic rate of £1.92 per hour. He is paid £2.88 for overtime.

(a) How much does he earn in a week, when he works 40 hours at the basic rate and 8 hours overtime?

(b) From this amount, he has to pay £18.84 for National Insurance and income tax. What is his take-home pay?

(c) He saves 10% of his take-home pay. How much does he save this week?

8 A train arrived in London at 1427. It was 33 minutes late. What time should it have arrived?

9

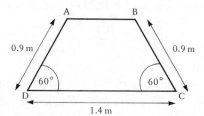

This is a rough sketch of a table.

(a) Use a scale of 1 cm ≡ $\frac{1}{10}$ m to make an accurate scale drawing.

(b) Use your drawing to find

    (i) the length of AB,

    (ii) the distance between the parallel lines AB and DC.

10

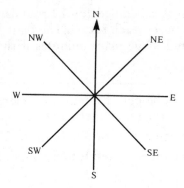

How many degrees are there

(a) turning clockwise from north to south-east,

(b) turning clockwise from south-east to west,

(c) turning anticlockwise from north-west to south,

(d) turning anticlockwise from south-west to north-east?

Revision Paper   **15**

1 Copy and complete this addition table.

+	2	4	6	8
3				11
5		9		
7			13	

2 The postage on a parcel is 47p. Can Sue pay the correct postage using only 4p stamps and 13p stamps?

3 A factory employs 520 people. Each person is paid £150 per week.

(a) Find the total weekly wage bill for the factory.

(b) The work-force is reduced by 10%. How many people work at the factory after the reduction?

(c) The weekly wage for each person is increased by £10. Find the new weekly wage bill for the factory, with the reduced work-force.

4 A boxing contest is scheduled for 12 rounds: 3 minutes each round, and 1 minute between each round. The fight finishes after 2 minutes of the ninth round. How many minutes is this after the start of the fight?

5 In an election for the club captain, 200 members voted. 40% voted for Nick Brain and the remainder voted for Sue Morgan.

(a) What percentage voted for Sue Morgan?

(b) How many members voted for Nick Brain?

6 An aeroplane from Cyprus is due to arrive at Birmingham Airport at 0214. Because of a strong head wind it arrives 35 minutes late. What time does it arrive?

7

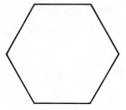

The diagram shows a regular hexagon. Show how several such hexagons (at least six) can be fitted together with no spaces in between. By considering the point where three hexagons come together, find the size of each angle in a regular hexagon.

8

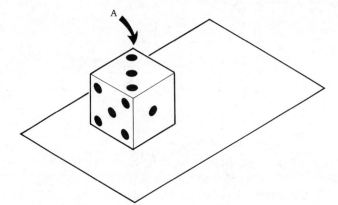

(a) What is the sum of the numbers on the opposite faces of a dice?

(b) What number is on the bottom of the dice?

(c) What is the sum of the numbers you can see in the diagram?

(d) What is the sum of the three faces you can see if you look at the dice from the other side A? (Remember that you can still see the top!)

9 Here are three Job Centre cards.

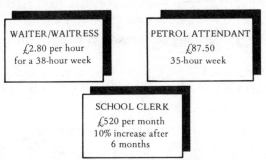

WAITER/WAITRESS
£2.80 per hour
for a 38-hour week

PETROL ATTENDANT
£87.50
35-hour week

SCHOOL CLERK
£520 per month
10% increase after
6 months

(a) How much does the waiter/waitress earn in a week?

(b) How much does the petrol attendant earn
   (i) per hour,
   (ii) in a year of 52 weeks?

(c) Javi got the job as the school clerk.
   (i) How much will he earn in his first 6 months?
   (ii) What is his monthly salary after 6 months?

10

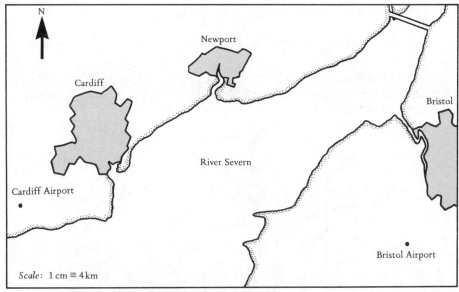

Scale: 1 cm ≡ 4 km

(a) Measure the distance on the map, to the nearest half centimetre, between Cardiff Airport and Bristol Airport.

(b) Use the scale given on the map to find the actual distance between these two airports.

(c) A plane leaves Cardiff for Paris, but has to call at Bristol. Use your protractor to find the bearing on which the pilot must fly from Cardiff to Bristol.

1 Find $11 \div 19$, giving your answer correct to the nearest hundredth.

2 Put the numbers 0.88, 0.71, 0.09 and 0.089 in order, smallest first.

3

		4
5	9	
	3	

Complete the magic square so that the numbers in every row, column and diagonal total 27.

4 There are 45 houses in a street numbered from 1 to 45. Odd numbers are on one side of the street; even numbers are on the other.

(a) How many houses have odd numbers?

(b) How many houses have even numbers?

5 The pictogram shows the method by which the fifth-year pupils come to school.

represents 5 pupils (head 1, arms and legs 1 each)

(a) How many pupils cycle to school?

(b) How many pupils are there in the fifth year?

(c) How many more pupils come by bus than by car?

6

In the diagram, Fred is 4 cm high and Paul, his son, is 3 cm high. Fred's real height is 160 cm. How tall is Paul?

7

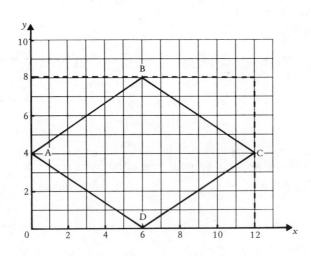

(a) What name do we give to quadrilateral ABCD?

(b) Find the area of this quadrilateral.

(*Hint*: Area of a triangle $= \frac{1}{2}$ Base $\times$ Height.)

8 To cook a chicken, the time required is 40 minutes per kilogram plus 20 minutes.

(a) How long should it take to cook a $3\frac{1}{2}$ kg chicken?

(b) Mr Hazell's chicken was nicely cooked after 1 hour 50 minutes. Estimate the mass of the chicken.

9 Study these hollow squares, and draw the next three in the pattern.

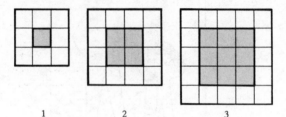

1   2   3

Copy and complete the table which shows the connection between the number of the square, the number of shaded squares, and the number of squares forming the hollow squares.

Number of square	1	2	3	4	5	6
Number of shaded squares	1	4				
Number of small squares forming the hollow square	8	12				

10 Mrs Cowley wants to prepare a meal for six people. She needs

12 slices of ham

18 potatoes

30 sprouts

6 carrots

What will she need to provide the same meal for

(a) nine people,   (b) four people?

Revision Paper   17

1 A teacher has 25 textbooks for a form with 32 pupils. If each pupil is to have one book, how many more are needed?

2 You are given that $V = abc$.
   (a) Find the value of V if $a = 2$, $b = 3$ and $c = 4$.
   (b) Find the value of c if $V = 60$, $a = 3$ and $b = 5$.

154

3 Linda has £1 to spend on 15p stamps.
   (a) How many stamps can she buy?
   (b) How much change will she get?

4

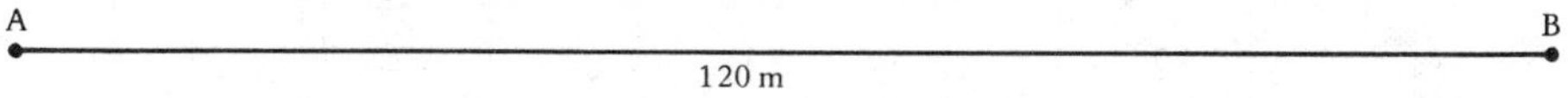

A ●————————————————————————————————————● B
                        120 m

The diagram shows a length of road, AB, which is 120 m long. The road has lights at A and B. Copy the diagram, and on it mark the positions of three new lights so that all five are equally spaced.

5 Construct a triangle XYZ in which XY = 10 cm, XZ = 7 cm and YZ = 11.5 cm. Measure each of the angles in this triangle, and hence find their sum. Is your answer what you expected?

6 Draw a diagram of
   (a) a parallelogram,   (b) a trapezium.

7 The cost of hiring a car for N days is £(20 + 10N).
   (a) How much will it cost to hire the car for
       (i) 2 days,
       (ii) 7 days?
   (b) For how many days do I hire the car if the cost is £60?

8 The table shows the shortest stopping distance, in feet, for a car with good tyres and brakes on a dry road. Copy and complete this table.

                Shortest stopping distances (in ft)

Speed (in m.p.h.)	Thinking distance	Braking distance	Overall stopping distance
20	20	20	40
30	30	45	75
40	40	80	
50		125	175
60		180	
70	70	245	

155

9   Look at this calendar.

Mon.	Tue.	Wed.	Thur.	Fri.	Sat.	Sun.
		1	2	3	4	5
6	7	8	9	10	11	12
13	14	15	16	17	18	19
20	21	22	23	24	25	26
27	28	29	30			

(a) Which month could this be – August, September or October?

(b) Yesterday was the ninth of the month. What will be the date a week tomorrow?

(c) Today is the 24th. What was the date a week last Saturday?

(d) The day after tomorrow is the third Wednesday of the month. What is the date today?

(e) The day before yesterday was the second Sunday of the month. What date will it be a week tomorrow?

10

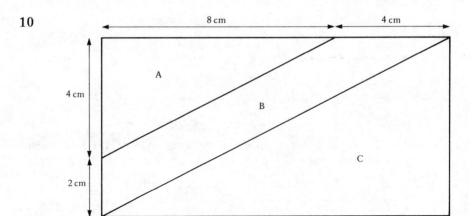

The diagram shows a rectangle divided into three areas marked A, B and C.

(a) Find the area of
   (i) A,   (ii) B,   (iii) C.

(b) What is the ratio of
   (i) the area of A to the area of C,
   (ii) the area of B to the area of C?

Revision Paper   18

1 (a) What is the place value of the 4 in the number 13.247?
   (b) What is the sum of 11.1, 2.09 and 0.55?

2 The shaded part of the diagram shows the net of a cube.

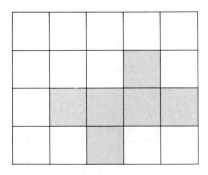

(a) What fraction of the diagram is shaded? (Give your answer in
    its simplest form.)
(b) Can a second net for a cube be drawn on the unshaded part of
    the diagram? If your answer is 'Yes', draw this net.

3 If $a = 2$, $b = -2$ and $c = 0$, find the value of
  (a) $a + b$ (b) $a - b$ (c) $ab + ac$ (d) abc

4 Eric uses a £1 coin to pay for a loaf of bread, costing 54 p, and two
  cakes costing 17 p each. How much change does he get?

5 Penelope measures the length of a lawn as 23.47 m. Write this length
  (a) correct to the nearest 5 m,
  (b) correct to the nearest tenth of a metre,
  (c) in centimetres.

6 A motorist travels from La Baule to Auray, a distance of 180 km.
  Find
  (a) the number of litres of petrol required for this journey if the car
      travels, on average, 12 km on each litre of petrol,
  (b) the cost of the petrol used at 40 p per litre,
  (c) the distance from La Baule to Auray in miles if 8 km ≡ 5 miles.

7 Jim has written three letters and addressed three envelopes. In how many different ways can he put all the three letters in the wrong envelopes? Label the envelopes A, B and C, the letters a, b and c and use the table.

	Envelopes		
	A	B	C
Letters	b	c	a

8 By putting in decimal points, give the 5 in each number the value of five hundredths.

(a) 245   (b) 0051   (c) 752

9

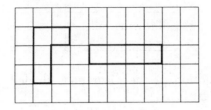

(a) Use two of each of these two shapes to make a shape that has four lines of symmetry. Show clearly with broken lines the position of these lines of symmetry.

(b) Use two of the left-hand shape to make a shape that has rotational symmetry of order 2.

10

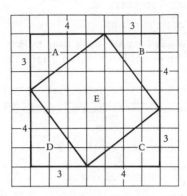

Look at the diagram which shows a square within a square.

(a) Does the diagram have an axis of symmetry?

(b) Does the diagram have rotational symmetry? If so, state the order.

(c) Find the area of the triangle marked A.

(d) Write down the area of each of the triangles marked B, C and D.

(e) Find the area of the large square.

(f) Use your answer to parts (c), (d) and (e) to find the area of the square marked E.

(g) What is the length of a side of the small square?

(h) Find the ratio of the length of a side of the small square to the length of a side of the large square.

(i) Find the ratio of the area of the small square to the area of the large square.

(j) Are your answers to parts (h) and (i) connected?

Revision Paper   19

1 (a) Complete the following bill.

> 5 lb of potatoes at 9 p per lb   ____
> _ lb of peas at 52 p per lb   1.56
> 3 lb of carrots at ____ p per lb   1.29
>
> Total   ____

(b) How much change will there be from a £10 note?

2 There were two candidates for the position of Head Girl in a school. The fifth-form votes were: Haines 136, Zeraschi 87, spoilt papers 15. Eight pupils failed to vote.

(a) How many fifth-form pupils voted?

(b) How many fifth-form pupils could have voted?

3

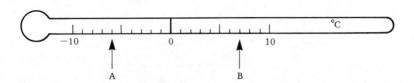

(a) What temperature does the arrow at A show?

(b) What temperature does the arrow at B show?

(c) What is the difference between the two temperatures?

4 A video recorder costs £420 if bought on hire-purchase. The cash price of the recorder is £360. If the hire-purchase agreement requires a deposit of £36 and 24 equal monthly payments, how much would be paid each month?

5

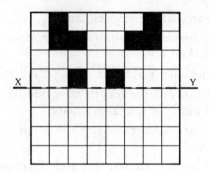

The diagram shows part of a crossword puzzle.

(a) Shade the squares below XY so that the figure is symmetrical about XY.

(b) How many eight-letter words are there in this puzzle?

6 The numbers

$$15, 17, 21, 31, 41, 42, 54, 83, 95, 108$$

are written on pieces of paper and placed in a bag. One number is now drawn at random. What is the probability that this number is

(a) less than 50,

(b) more than 50,

(c) more than 100,

(d) a prime number?

7

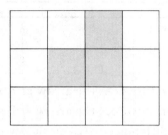

(a) What fraction of this rectangle is shaded?

(b) Shade more squares so that $\frac{2}{3}$ of the rectangle is shaded *and* the completed figure is symmetrical about a horizontal line. Show the position of this line.

8 Three brothers go out to dinner. Their total bill is £13.50. If they each agree to pay the same, how much does each pay? One brother finds that he has left his money at home. How much extra must each of the other two pay to cover their brother's share?

9

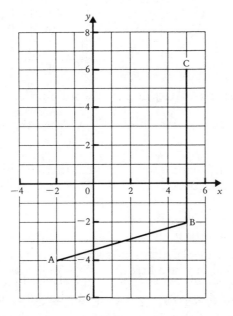

(a) Write the coordinates of each of the points A, B and C.

(b) Copy the diagram and mark a point D, so that ABCD is a parallelogram. Write the coordinates of the point D.

10 There are six players in the school chess team. Each player plays each of the other five. Use the table to find out how many matches are played.

	Ann	Ben	Colin	Dave	Eddy	Frank
Ann						
Ben						
Colin						
Dave						
Eddy						
Frank						

1   In a game of darts, Joe had three throws. These scored a double 13, a treble 16 and a 3. What is his total score with the three darts?

2

(a) What kind of triangle is drawn opposite?

(b) Complete the following statement.

$$2x + y = \qquad °$$

(c) If $x = 65°$, find y.

(d) If $y = 80°$, find x.

3   (a) If $1\,kg = 2.2\,lb$ convert
    (i) 10 kg into pounds,   (ii) 88 lbs into kilograms.
    (b) If 1 gallon $= 4.5$ litres convert
    (i) 12 gallons into litres,   (ii) 36 litres into gallons.

4   Trudy Kelly earns £9872 a year. When she retires, she will be paid a pension of $\frac{3}{8}$ of this salary. What pension will she get?

5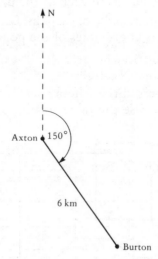

The diagram shows the positions of Axton and Burton. Burton is 6 km from Axton, on a bearing of 150°. A third town, Cadbury, is 13 km from Burton on a bearing of 040°. Make a scale diagram to show the positions of the three places, using 1 cm to represent 1 km. Use your diagram to find the distance and direction of Cadbury from Axton.

6   For this solid write
    (a) the number of faces,
    (b) the number of edges,
    (c) the number of vertices.

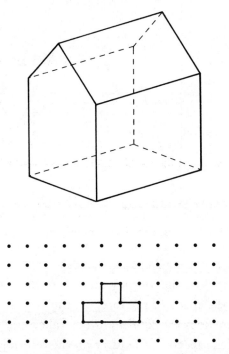

7

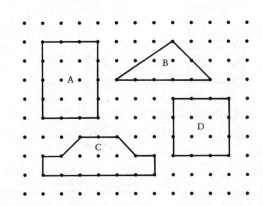

A tessellation is to be drawn on this grid using more shapes like the
one given. Show, by drawing at least eight more of these shapes, how
a regular pattern can be built up.

8

(a) Find the area of each of the shapes marked A, B, C and D.
(b) Which two have equal areas?

9   The graph shows the journey of a lorry from Derby to Leeds and back.

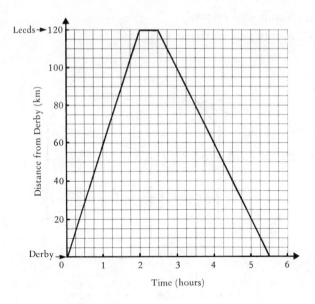

(a) How far is it from Derby to Leeds?
(b) How long does the journey take?
(c) What is the speed of the lorry on the outward journey?
(d) How long does the return journey take?
(e) What is the speed of the lorry on the return journey?

10

(a) What is the cost of 50 g in the smaller jar?
(b) What is the cost of 50 g in the larger jar?
(c) Which jar is the better value?

Part 3: Multiple Choice Questions 1–8

In the following exercises, you are given several alternative answers. In each case, write the letter that corresponds to the correct answer.

Multiple Choice Questions   **1**

1   Which one of these distances is the closest approximation to 76 mm?

    A   0.08 m   B   0.07 m   C   0.7 m   D   0.80 m

2   $\frac{2}{5}$ expressed as a decimal is

    A   0.4   B $\frac{4}{10}$ C   0.25   D   0.2

3   Given that 1 mile is roughly 1.6 km, the approximate value of 30 miles is

    A   30 km   B   48 km   C   19 km   D   24 km

4   If $\dfrac{x}{3} = 7$ the value of x is

    A   4   B   21   C $2\frac{1}{3}$ D $\frac{3}{7}$

5   The cooking time for a joint of meat is 20 minutes per pound plus 20 minutes. The time needed to cook a joint weighing $4\frac{1}{2}$ lb is

    A   80 minutes   B   90 minutes

    C   100 minutes   D   110 minutes

6

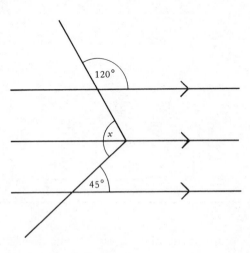

The size of the angle marked x is

    A   15°   B   95°   C   105°   D   60°

7

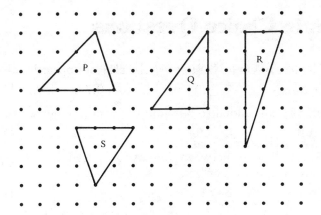

Look at the areas of these triangles. Which triangle is the odd one out?

A P   B Q   C R   D S

8 The first lesson of a school day starts at 9.15 a.m. and lasts for 50 minutes. It finishes at

A 9.55 a.m.   B 10.05 a.m.   C 10.15 a.m.   D 10.10 a.m.

9 Correct to the nearest $\frac{1}{2}$ litre, the approximate value of 15.758 litres is

A 15 litres   B $15\frac{1}{2}$ litres   C 16 litres   D 15.8 litres

10

The temperature at the place shown in the diagram is probably about

A 28 °F   B 82 °F   C 160 °F   D 48 °F

Multiple Choice Questions 2

1 84% expressed as a fraction in its lowest terms is

   A $\frac{4}{5}$ B $\frac{21}{25}$ C $\frac{42}{50}$ D $\frac{84}{100}$

2 When 54 cm is added to 540 mm the total, in metres, is

   A 1.08   B 5.94   C 0.594   D 108

3 £3.50 is divided between Mandy and Len in the ratio 3:4. The amount of money Len gets is

   A 50p   B £1.50   C £2   D £2.50

4 The price of a car is £11 000 plus VAT at 15%. The total price of the car, including VAT is

   A £1650   B £9350   C £12 650   D £11 500

5 Jenni takes 15 minutes to walk the 1 km to school. Her average walking speed is

   A 4 km/hour   B 8 km/hour   C 6 km/hour   D $4\frac{1}{2}$ km/hour

6

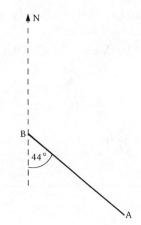

The bearing of A from B is

   A 044°   B 156°   C 136°   D 224°

7

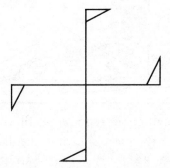

This figure has rotational symmetry of order

   A 1   B 2   C 3   D 4

8

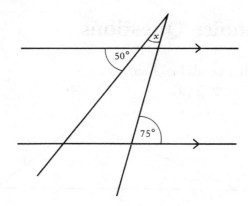

The size of the angle marked x is

A 75°   B 50°   C 25°   D 15°

9 The temperature at 6 a.m. was $-7\,°C$. By 1 p.m. it had gone up by $9\,°C$. The temperature at 1 p.m. was

A 16 °C   B $-16\,°C$ C 2 °C   D 9 °C

10

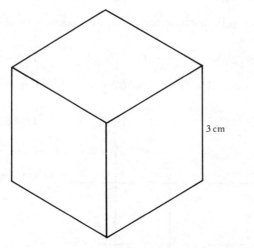

The number of small cubes required to fill the space within the large cube is

A 3   B 9   C 18   D 27

Multiple Choice Questions

1   The number of seconds in 4 hours is

    A 2400   B 240   C 1440   D 14 400

2

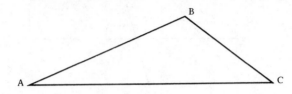

In triangle ABC, the angle ABC is

    A acute   B reflex   C obtuse   D a right angle

3   The cost of a $1\frac{1}{2}$ kg bag of flour is 48p. The cost of 250 g of this flour is

    A 6p   B 8p   C 10p   D 12p

4   Which of these distances is the closest approximation to 0.4 m?

    A 36 cm   B 47 cm   C 43 cm   D 39 cm

5   Given that $2x + 1 = 19$, the value of x is

    A 10   B 9   C 16   D 20

6   The mean of 14, 8, 9, 16 and 28 is

    A 16   B 18   C 15   D 14

7   When a shopkeeper sells a chair for £72, he makes a profit of £12. His percentage profit is

    A 16.7%   B 20%   C 25%   D 14.3%

8   Sid Showers was born in 1912. He was 63 years old when he died. He died in

    A 1976   B 1977   C 1978   D 1979

9

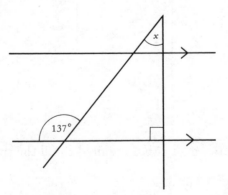

The value of the angle marked x is

    A 17°   B 43°   C 47°   D 73°

10 A rectangular cold water tank is 4 m long, 3 m wide and 2 m deep.

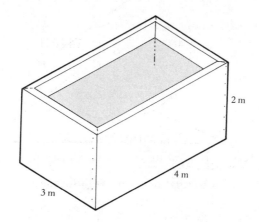

The volume of this tank is

A 40 m³   B 24 m³   C 28 m³   D 9 m³

Multiple Choice Questions   4

1 If one of the base angles of an isosceles triangle is 56°, the other angles in the triangle are

   A 62° and 62°   B 56° and 68°   C 56° and 88°   D 56° and 62°

2 Mike walks to school at an average speed of 6 km/hour. He takes 12 minutes. The distance from his home to school is

   A 0.6 km   B 0.5 km   C 1.2 km   D 1 km

3 The value of $12^2 - 5^2$ is

   A 193   B 49   C 119   D 139

4 In a sale, a furniture store gives a discount of 20%. The sale price of a dining suite originally marked £1200 is

   A £1000   B £1440   C £960   D £1180

5

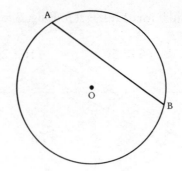

The line AB in the circle, centre O is called

A a diameter   B a radius   C a tangent   D a chord

6 On the plan of a bungalow, 1 cm represents 1 m. In ratio form, the scale of the plan is

A 1:100   B 1:10   C 10:1   D 100:1

7 Given that $\dfrac{x-3}{4} = 2$, the value of x is

A 5   B $2\frac{3}{4}$ C 24   D 11

8

The temperature at the place shown in the diagram is probably about

A 29 °C   B 92 °C   C 160 °C   D 60 °C

9

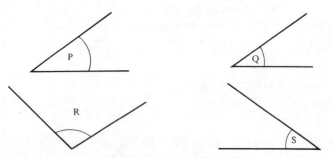

Paul drew four angles. The largest angle is

A P   B Q   C R   D S

172

10   If £550 is invested for 3 years at 9% per year, the simple interest earned is

A £135   B £698.50   C £162.26   D £148.50

Multiple Choice Questions   **5**

1

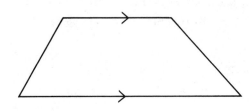

The name given to this quadrilateral is

A a rectangle   B a trapezium
C a parallelogram   D a square

2

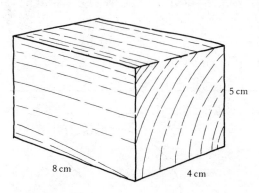

The volume of this wooden block is

A $17 \, cm^3$ B $60 \, cm^3$ C $72 \, cm^3$ D $160 \, cm^3$

3   Which ratio is *not* the same as $48:32$?

A $24:16$ B $15:10$ C $16:24$ D $21:14$

4 The tally chart shows the distribution of the colour of hair of 24
   pupils.

Black	ⅢⅢ
Fair	ⅢⅢ |||
Ginger	||
Brunnette	ⅢⅢ ||||

What fraction of the pupils have fair hair?

A $\frac{1}{4}$ B $\frac{3}{8}$ C $\frac{1}{6}$ D $\frac{1}{3}$

5 Which of these distances is the closest approximation to 0.6 m?

A 625 mm   B 62 cm   C 595 mm   D 59 cm

6 The number 156.55, when written correct to the nearest 10 is

A 150   B 160   C 200   D 156.6

7 When a record sells at a profit of 50%, its price is £6. The cost price
   of the record was

A £4   B £9   C £6   D £3

8

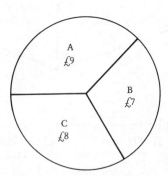

The reading on this scale is

A 7.2   B 4.7   C 7.4   D 3.7

9

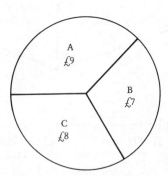

In the pie chart, the angle representing C should be

A 135°   B 105°   C 120°   D 130°

10

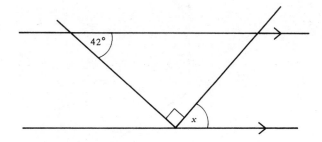

The size of the angle marked x is

A 42° B 48° C 138° D 45°

Multiple Choice Questions 6

1

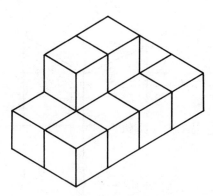

The number of cubes in this stack is

A 10 B 8 C 12 D 9

2 Which one of the following quadrilaterals has exactly one axis of symmetry?

A a rectangle B a rhombus
C a parallelogram D a kite

3 The value of $2^2 + 4^2$ is

A 36 B 12 C 18 D 20

4 When insuring the contents of my house, an insurance company charges 80p for each £100 insured. I estimate that the contents of my house are worth £10 000. The amount I must pay the insurance company is

A £8 B £80 C £800 D £8000

5

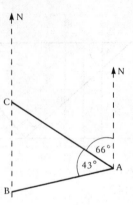

The bearing of B from A is

A 109°   B 071°   C 251°   D 289°

6

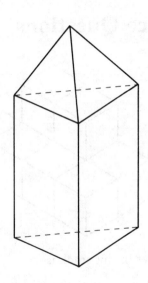

A solid is formed by placing a triangular pyramid on top of a triangular prism. The number of edges the solid has is

A 10   B 12   C 9   D 11

7 The mode of the numbers 9, 3, 7, 3, 8 and 4 is

A 9   B 7   C 6   D 3

8 Ajit left home at 0838 and arrived in school at 0905. The time he took to get to school was

A 51 minutes   B 31 minutes   C 67 minutes   D 27 minutes

9

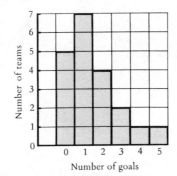

Number of teams (y-axis)
Number of goals (x-axis)

The bar chart shows the number of goals scored by the teams in a league. The total number of goals scored was

A 30   B 40   C 45   D 36

10   The scale of a plan is 1 cm to 5 cm. The actual length of the top of a desk is 130 cm. On the plan the length is

A 650 cm   B 26 cm   C 260 cm   D 2.6 cm

Multiple Choice Questions   7

1

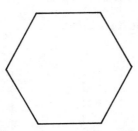

The name given to this shape is

A a rhombus   B a pentagon   C an octagon   D a hexagon

2   The number of edges on a square pyramid is

A 4   B 8   C 5   D 7

3   S55°E is exactly the same direction as

A 055°   B 235°   C 305°   D 125°

4

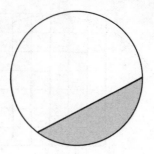

The part of this circle that is shaded is called

A a sector   B a segment   C a chord   D a semicircle

5 Which ratio is the same as $36:45$?

A $16:20$ B $4:9$ C $45:54$ D $90:72$

6 $24a \times 6a$ simplifies to

A $144a^2$ B $144a$ C $30a$ D $30a^2$

7 If £1 is worth \$1.8 dollars, the equivalent value of \$63 is

A £45   B £113.40   C £35   D £54

8 A rectangular field is a metres long and b metres wide. The perimeter of this field, in metres, is

A $2a + 2b$ B $a + b$ C $2ab$ D ab

9 The net that will not form a cube is

A

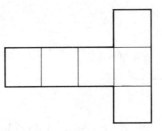

B

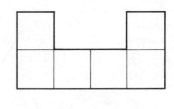

C

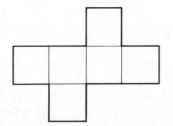

D

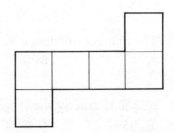

10

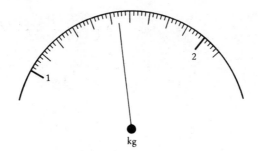

kg

The reading on this dial is

A 1.27 kg   B 1.57 kg   C 1.52 kg   D 1.54 kg

Multiple Choice Questions   **8**

1   The scale of a map is 1 cm represents 1 km. As a ratio this scale is
    A 1 : 100 000   B 1 : 10 000   C 1 : 1000   D 1 : 100

2   A desk is 1.42 m long. The length of this desk in millimetres is
    A 14 200   B 14.2   C 142   D 1420

3   Toothpaste is sold in four sizes. The best buy is
    A 50 g for 18 p   B 100 g for 34 p
    C 150 g for 48 p   D 250 g for 84 p

4   Jane earns £80 a week. She is given a 6% pay rise. Her new weekly
    wage is
    A £86   B £88.40   C £84.80   D £88

5

      1000   100   10   1

The reading on this gas meter is

    A 6586   B 6686   C 6696   D 7697

6   If $x = 3$, the value of $2x^2 - 4$ is
    A 32   B 14   C 18   D 10

7   The size of each angle of a regular hexagon is
    A 72°   B 135°   C 108°   D 120°

8
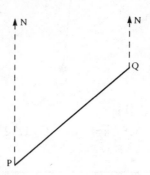

If the bearing of P from Q is 230°, the bearing of Q from P is
    A 230°   B 050°   C 130°   D 040°

9
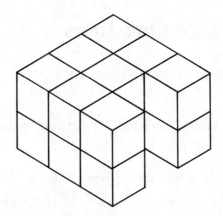

The number of small cubes making up this stack is
    A 12   B 16   C 18   D 14

10
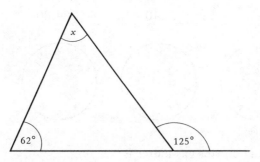

The size of the angle marked x is
    A 62°   B 63°   C 55°   D 62½°

Part 4:   Aural Tests 1–10

It is not intended that you should work these tests out as you read the book. Get someone to read each question to you. Do not use a calculator. You should have nothing on your desk other than a pencil (or a pen) and paper. Each question will be read twice, and you will have a reasonable amount of time to write your answer. The whole test should take less than ten minutes.

Aural Test   1

1   How many months are there in a year?

2   How many minutes are there in an hour?

3   How many hours are there from eight o'clock in the morning until six o'clock in the evening?

4   Write one-half as a decimal.

5   Write one thousand and four hundred in figures.

6   Tickets for a concert cost five pounds each. What is the cost of seven tickets?

7   How many corners has a cube?

8   The price of a motorcycle is three thousand and fifty pounds. Write this price in figures.

9   Colin is paid two pounds fifty an hour. How much should he be paid for eight hours' work?

10 In a golf competition, there are three players in each team. If there are eight teams, how many golfers are there?

11 Jim is playing darts. He throws treble nineteen. What does he score?

12 A packet of screws costs twenty-three pence. How much do ten packets cost?

Aural Test   2

1   What is one-half of twelve?

2   What is the sum of the three angles in a triangle?

3   Write fifty per cent as a decimal.

4   Write one hundred and six in figures.

5   Which is longer — one inch or two centimetres?

6   Is nineteen ninety-two a leap year?

7   What is the next month after September?

8   Bus fares are increased by ten per cent. The old fare was eighty pence. What is the new fare?

182

9   In a sports competition, there are six players in each team. Forty-two players take part in the competition. How many teams are there?

10   A meal costs seven pounds. Peter decides to leave a ten per cent tip. How much is the tip?

11   Doris works for seven hours and gets paid twenty-eight pounds. How much is this per hour?

12   Vernon tosses a coin. What is the probability that it lands 'heads up'?

Aural Test   3

1   Write one-quarter as a percentage.

2   How many faces does a cube have?

3   How many sides does a square have?

4   I stand facing north and turn to look south. What angle have I turned through?

5   Thirty-six chocolates are shared equally amongst nine children. How many does each child get?

6   How many corners has a cuboid?

7   Write down any decimal that lies between nought point two and nought point two five.

8   School starts at nine a.m. It takes me twelve minutes to walk to school. I want to be in school five minutes early. What time should I leave home?

9   In three visits to the table, a snooker player scored thirty, forty-two and six. What was her average score?

10   Gary's meals costs two pounds, seventy-five pence. He pays with a five-pound note. How much change should he get?

11   If ten pounds are equivalent to seventeen dollars, how many dollars will I get for one pound?

12   The notice in a sale says 'Ten per cent off'. How much should I pay for a suit marked sixty pounds?

Aural Test 4

1 What is one-half of two and a half?

2 How many days are there in the month of April?

3 What is the sum of the first four whole numbers?

4 Which is further — one mile or one kilometre?

5 Tickets for an international match cost twelve pounds each. What is the cost of four tickets?

6 I arrive at the station at three forty-two p.m., and I see that the next train is due at four twelve p.m. How many minutes should I have to wait?

7 Forty-two thousand and twenty spectators attended a football match. Write this number in figures.

8 Sixty-four per cent of the pupils in my class study physics. What percentage do not study physics?

9 In a game of darts, I score sixty-eight with my first three darts. If I start with three hundred and one, what will my new total be when the sixty-eight has been subtracted?

10 Morning school starts at nine and finishes at twelve fifteen. How long is morning school?

11 Tyres for my car cost thirty-three pounds each. How much will four new tyres cost me?

12 Two angles of a triangle are fifty degrees and ninety-five degrees. Write the size of the third angle.

Aural Test 5

1 Write fifty-two correct to the nearest ten.

2 Is nineteen ninety-seven a leap year?

3 Does the month of September have thirty days?

4 I bought three books. The first cost two pounds, the second five pounds, and the third six pounds, forty pence. How much did I spend altogether?

5 The distance between two railway stations is five point one eight kilometres. Write down this distance, in kilometres, correct to one decimal place.

6   How many minutes are there in one and a half hours?

7   How many faces does a triangular prism have?

8   Two is a prime number. Write down the next two prime numbers.

9   How many corners are there in a square?

10   Morning school ends at twelve and afternoon school starts at one fifteen. How long is the lunch break?

11   One in ten of the eggs in a basket are cracked. There are one hundred eggs in the basket. How many are cracked?

12   The petrol tank of a car is half-full. The tank is filled by adding six gallons. How much will the tank hold?

Aural Test   6

1   Write forty-nine correct to the nearest five.

2   What is the cost of three loaves of bread at sixty-four pence each?

3   Kate takes fourteen minutes to walk to school. She leaves home at eight twenty-two a.m. At what time should she arrive at school?

4   Is one kilogram heavier than two pounds?

5   What is the next month after March?

6   Norma is an only child. She is twelve years old. Her father is forty-eight and her mother is forty-five. What is the average age of the family?

7   Meg bought a one kilogram bag of sugar. She used seven hundred and eighty grams of it. How many grams did she have left?

8   In a class, each pupil has eight exercise books. There are twenty-five pupils in the class. How many exercise books do they have altogether?

9   A piece of wood is one point seven metres long. How many centimetres is this?

10   Five jars of coffee cost five pounds, forty pence. How much does one jar cost?

11   George has four coins. Their total value is thirty-two pence. What could the coins be?

12   Subtract the difference between twenty and twelve from the sum of eight and fourteen.

Aural Test 7

1 Write the area, in square metres, of a rectangular carpet measuring four metres by three and a half metres.

2 Write, as a single number, six squared minus ten.

3 How many corners has a rectangular block?

4 John has a one metre length of wood. He cuts sixty-seven centimetres off. What length of wood remains?

5 In a team, there are four boys and six girls. What percentage of the team are girls?

6 Which month of the year has the least number of days?

7 Janet stands facing west. She turns clockwise through ninety degrees. In what direction is she facing?

8 Peter buys a newspaper costing twenty-five pence and a magazine costing fifty pence. How much change will he get from one pound?

9 Three tins of beans cost fifty-seven pence. How much does one cost?

10 There are eight boys and sixteen girls in a class. A pupil is chosen at random. What is the probability that the pupil chosen is a boy?

11 Sixty per cent of the audience at a concert are female. There are five hundred people in the audience. How many males attend the concert?

12 Write the number that is exactly half-way between twelve and twenty-six.

Aural Test 8

1 Write seventy-five correct to the nearest ten.

2 How many eighteen pence stamps can I buy for fifty pence? How much change do I get?

3 Two in every three of the pupils in a class are girls. There are twenty girls. How many pupils are there in the class?

4 What is the month immediately before June?

5 Train fares are increased by ten per cent. The old fare was one pound forty. How much is the increase?

6 The distance around a motor racing circuit is three point four seven miles. Write this distance, in miles, correct to one decimal place.

7 Ron pays eight thousand pounds for a car. He believes it will go down in value by twenty-five per cent during the first year. How much should it be worth when it is one year old?

8 Helen leaves home to go to work at eight a.m. and gets back home at five forty five p.m. How long is she away from home?

9 Two angles in a triangle are equal. The third angle is fifty degrees. Find the value of each of the equal angles.

10 A joint of meat weighs five pounds. How much does it cost, if the price of each pound is one pound twenty?

11 A car does about forty miles to the gallon. Estimate, to the nearest gallon, the number of gallons needed for a journey of one hundred and fifty-two miles.

12 Vera throws a dice. What is the probability that she scores four?

Aural Test 9

1 I bought two records. One cost three pounds, sixty pence and the other cost one pound, seventy pence. How much did I spend altogether?

2 A rectangle is seven centimetres long and five centimetres wide. What is the perimeter of this rectangle?

3 Today is Wednesday, the fourth of May. What will the date be a week tomorrow?

4 Tyrone drives for two hours at a steady speed of forty-two miles per hour. How far will he travel?

5 How many minutes are there in a quarter of an hour?

6 What is the month three months after March?

7 Fred was born in nineteen thirty. In which year did he celebrate his fiftieth birthday?

8 Kerry stands facing east. He turns through half a turn. In which direction is he now facing?

9 In a game of darts, I score ninety-five with my first three darts. If I start with five hundred and one, what will my new total be when ninety-five has been subtracted?

10 Write the number that is exactly half-way between one point four and two point six.

11 Fifty per cent of all the money I have is fifty-pence. How much money do I have?

12 Twelve lamp standards in a street are each fifty metres apart. How far is it from the first lamp standard to the last?

Aural Test

1 Tickets for a musical cost eight pounds each. What is the cost of six tickets?

2 What is one-third of eighteen?

3 Twelve pounds of potatoes cost one pound and eight pence. How much is this per pound?

4 Tomorrow is the twentieth of October. What was the date yesterday?

5 Joan is playing darts. With her first three darts she scores fourteen, double six and treble twelve. How many does she score altogether with the three darts?

6 Twenty-eight sweets are shared equally amongst five sisters. How many sweets does each sister get? How many sweets are left over?

7 Paul is paid time and a half for overtime. His basic hourly pay is three pounds. How much does he get paid for two hours' overtime?

8 What is the perimeter of a rectangle measuring eight inches by six inches?

9 What is two minus three-quarters?

10 There are twice as many girls as boys in a class. If there are twenty-four pupils altogether, how many boys are there?

11 How many centimetres is sixty-seven centimetres short of one metre?

12 What is the smallest whole number that must be added to twenty-three to make the answer exactly divisible by five?
